MACMILLAN/McGRAW-HILL

TAKS
Preparation
and
Practice
Book

for
Reading and Writing

D1097593

Grade 4

Emilio Coceres

Macmillan
McGraw-Hill

New York

PHOTOGRAPHY CREDITS: All photos by PhotoDisc except as noted below.

86: m. Royalty-free Corbis. 191: b. Royalty-free Corbis. 103: b.r. Royalty-free Corbis

Macmillan/McGraw-Hill
A Division of The McGraw-Hill Companies

Published by Macmillan/McGraw-Hill, of McGraw-Hill Education, a division of The McGraw-Hill
Companies, Inc., Two Penn Plaza, New York, New York 10121.

Macmillan/McGraw-Hill
Two Penn Plaza
New York, New York 10121

Printed in the United States of America

11 021 08

CONTENTS

INTRODUCTION

This year, you will take the Texas Assessment of Knowledge and Skills (TAKS) in reading and writing. The TAKS is a series of exams that will test your knowledge of reading, writing, mathematics, science, and social studies. This book will help you prepare for the TAKS in reading and writing.

One book, however, cannot tell you everything you need to know about reading and writing skills to do well on the test. After all, you have been learning and studying these skills since the first grade. What this book will do is give you a lot of practice answering the kinds of multiple-choice questions that are on the TAKS reading and writing tests.

You probably have answered these kinds of questions before. On the following pages, you will learn ways to answer these questions effectively and accurately. In addition, you will review how to read and interpret the kinds of reading selections that you will encounter on the TAKS. With your teacher and classmates, you will review the skills that you will use to answer the questions on the TAKS in reading and writing. You will also take two practice tests with the same kinds of questions as the reading and writing tests. By the time you reach the end of this book, you will feel more confident and prepared to take the tests. Then you can really show what you know.

About This Book

There are three parts to this book:

1. **Test-Taking Strategies**—This section will give you some test-taking tips for the TAKS in reading and writing.

2. **Practice Exercises**—These exercises will review the skills you need to know for the tests. They will also give you valuable practice answering the different types of questions that you might see on the TAKS.

3. **Practice Tests**—The practice tests are just like the real TAKS reading and writing tests. You will take the practice tests twice: first near the beginning of the year, then near the end of the year.

TEST-TAKING STRATEGIES

Paragraph Labeling

On the TAKS reading and writing tests, you do not have to memorize the information you read in the selections. You can always go back to find the information you need.

Paragraph labeling can help you find information quickly. Write a few words in the margin that tell what the paragraph is about.

Paragraph Labeling with Informational Selections

Sometimes you will read informational selections on the test. With these types of selections, you can label each paragraph because each paragraph introduces a new idea.

Read the informational selection below. When you are finished reading each paragraph, write a label on the line next to it.

Early Submarines

1   A submarine is a ship that travels underwater. Did you know that the first successful submarine was built in 1620? This is the same year that the Pilgrims settled in America. _____

2   About 150 years later, an American student designed the *Turtle*. This one-man sub was powered by turning a crank. In 1776, the *Turtle* tried to sink a British ship but failed. _____

3   In 1864, the Confederates in the Civil War used the *Hunley*. This time the submarine attack was successful. The *Hunley* sank a large Union ship. However, the submarine also sank. _____

4   The first modern submarine was built in 1898 by John Holland. He sold his invention to the navy. This submarine, named the U.S.S. *Holland*, was 54 feet long. It used a gasoline-powered engine to travel above the water. For traveling underwater, it ran on battery-powered motors. _____

Paragraph Labeling with Literary Selections

Literary selections usually contain a lot of dialogue, or talking. These selections have so many paragraphs that it does not make sense to label each one. For these selections, you should only write a label after a new event or idea is introduced.

Read the selection below. Write a paragraph label on the lines provided.

The Mountain Cabin

1   When Chen-li and her parents set out for the mountain cabin they had rented, the afternoon was bright and the air a bit chilly. By the time they finished the long drive, it was dark. Low clouds covered the landscape. There was nothing to see, so they unloaded their car, had supper, and went to bed.

_____

_____

_____

2   Chen-li had never been to the mountains before. "I wonder what a mountain looks like," she thought as she lay in bed trying to fall asleep. "I've seen pictures of mountains," she thought, "but the highest hill I've seen is the one in the park. A real mountain must look very different."

_____

_____

3   Outside her window Chen-li heard rustling noises. She got up to peer outside. Unfortunately, a thick fog made it hard for her to see anything. "Is it the wind in the trees I hear?" she asked herself. "Or is it an animal? Maybe it's a bear!" Frightened, Chen-li jumped back in bed and pulled the covers over her head.

_____

_____

4   The next morning, bright sunlight shone through Chen-li's window and woke her up. "Wow!" she thought. "The clouds and fog are completely gone. Now I'll be able to see my first mountain!"

5   She ran to the window to look. Outside, she saw a spectacular view. Below the cabin lay a deep valley and a rushing river. In the distance was a range of huge mountains, with tall peaks blanketed in snow. Their rocky slopes were covered with thick forests of fir trees. To Chen-li, it was the most beautiful sight she had ever seen.

_____

_____

_____

Answering Multiple-Choice Questions

Return to the selection about early submarines on page 1.

Some multiple-choice questions will ask you about the entire selection. For example:

Which of the following is the best summary of the story?

Other multiple-choice questions will ask you about one part of the selection. The numbers in front of the paragraphs (or sentences on writing tests) will help you with this type of question. For example:

In paragraph 2, the author explains the Turtle *was powered by—*

The numbers allow you to quickly go back and reread the paragraph (or sentence) that will help you find the answer. Two other tools can help you find information quickly:

1. Key words
2. Paragraph labels

Key words are the words in a question that point you toward the information you need. Skim the selection, looking for those words. Then read to find the information needed for the question.

Underline the key words in the following question.

In paragraph 2, the author explains the Turtle *was powered by—*

Now go back to paragraph 2 of the selection about early submarines on page 1 and use the key words to find the sentence that contains the answer. Circle this sentence.

Paragraph labels can also help you answer questions. If you wrote *Turtle* as the label for the second paragraph of the selection about submarines, you could find the information quickly.

Paragraph and sentence numbers, key words, and paragraph labels will help you find answers without having to reread the whole selection. Of course, reading the selection carefully the first time will give you a good idea of what it is about.

Labels help you find things quickly.

Practice using key words.

Go back and reread the selection about submarines on page 1. Use key words and paragraph labels to help you answer the following questions. Fill in the correct circle for each question at the bottom of the page.

1   When was the first successful submarine attack?

     What are the key words in this question?

     _____

     What paragraph can you look in to help you find the answer?

     _____

Now choose the correct answer.

     A   1620

     B   1776

     C   1864

     D   1898

Now try another question. Underline the key words. Then return to the selection to look for the correct answer.

2   What event also occurred the same year the first submarine was built?

     A   The Pilgrims settled in America.

     B   The *Turtle* tried to sink a British ship.

     C   The Civil War occurred.

     D   The invention was sold to the navy.

| 1 | Ⓐ | Ⓑ | Ⓒ | Ⓓ |
| 2 | Ⓐ | Ⓑ | Ⓒ | Ⓓ |

Process of Elimination

Another technique you can use when answering multiple-choice questions is to rule out answers you know are wrong. This technique is called the **process of elimination.**

Try this example. This paragraph was taken from a longer selection. Read it and answer the question that follows.

Laura stormed up the stairs and through the front door. She slammed the door behind her and threw her backpack onto the living room sofa. Her mother put down her newspaper and looked up in surprise. "I have had it with that pesky Roberta!" Laura proclaimed in a loud voice.

1   The word pesky means—

   A   kind

   B   mean

   C   annoying

   D   friendly

Do you know what the word *pesky* means? If not, use the process of elimination to improve your chances of choosing the correct answer.

In the selection, Laura is obviously upset. It says she *stormed* up the stairs and *slammed* the door. Obviously Roberta has done something that Laura doesn't like, so we know that Laura would never describe Roberta as *kind* or *friendly*. So answer choices (A), *kind,* and (D), *friendly,* must be wrong.

That leaves only answer choices (B), *mean,* and (C), *annoying*. The process of elimination has helped because you now have to pick between only two answer choices instead of four. So even if you still don't know what *pesky* means, just take your best guess. With only two choices remaining, you have a much better chance of picking the correct one.

The answer to the question is (C), *annoying*.

Use the process of elimination on every multiple-choice question. Even if you can get rid of only one answer choice, the process of elimination makes choosing the correct answer easier.

Practice using the process of elimination.

Read the short selection below.

In the 1800s, there were no telephones, no computers, and no fax machines. If people wanted to communicate with someone far away, they had to write letters and send them by post. It could take a very long time to receive a letter in the mail. Around this time, Samuel Morse created the Morse code. Morse made up a language that could be communicated by telegraph. This system of communicating through wires is similar to our modern telephones. Morse gave each letter of the alphabet a code that consisted of a combination of long or short taps—dots or dashes. Telegraph offices would tap in people's messages using the dots and dashes. On the other end, another telegraph office would receive the dots and dashes and translate them back into words. Morse code became a popular way to send important messages to people far away.

Now answer the multiple-choice question, using the process of elimination. Cross out the answer choices that mention a minor detail from the selection. Then choose the correct answer from the choices that are left. Fill in the correct circle at the bottom of the page.

1   Which of the following sentences best tells what this paragraph is about?

   A   In the 1800s, people communicated by sending letters.

   B   Morse code became the quickest way to communicate with people far away.

   C   Morse code is a language made up of dots and dashes.

   D   Telegraph offices tapped in people's messages.

TEST-TAKING TIP   Use the process of elimination for all multiple-choice questions. It will improve your chances of choosing the correct answer.

Test-Taking Strategies • Grade 4

TAKS WRITING TEST

The TAKS writing test is given in two parts: a revising and editing part (Multiple-Choice Section) and a written composition (Writing to a Prompt).

Revising and Editing

In this part of the writing test, you will answer multiple-choice questions on how a sentence or paragraph might be improved or corrected.

Read the selection. Try to get a sense of what ideas the writer is trying to communicate.

Reread the selection and **underline** sentences that seem to be off the central idea of the paragraph, or in the wrong place.

Reread the selection again and **circle** any sentence fragments or incorrect grammar, spelling, or punctuation.

Keera has written a book report about one of her favorite books. Read Keera's report. Then reread it two times and underline or circle any errors you find.

Up, Up, and Away!

(1) *"The Twenty-One Balloons"* is about a professor by the name of William Sherman. (2) William wanted to get away from all civilization for one whole year. (3) He planned on traveling by a giant hot-air balloon! (4) A hot-air balloon is filled with gas and carries people in a basket. (5) Off he went exploring the skys. (6) I took a ride in a hot-air balloon last summer.

(7) On the first day of his voyage, a flock of seagulls attacks his balloon! (8) Luckily his balloon landed on an island. (9) It was paradise! (10) The people were also interesting! (11) He is just getting used to it when a volcano erupts. (12) Do you want to know if he survives? (13) You'll have to read this book.

Practice using your editing notes.

Use your editing notes on page 7 to find the information that will help you answer the following questions. Then fill in the correct circle for each question at the bottom of the page.

1 What change, if any, should be made in sentence 5?

   A Change *Off* to **off**

   B Change *skys* to **skies**

   C Change *exploring* to **explorring**

   D Make no change

What are the key words in the question?

_____

Should you look for circled words or underlined sentences?

_____

Now try two other questions. Underline the key words in each question below, then return to the selection to look for the correct answer.

2 What is the **BEST** way to rewrite the ideas in sentence 1?

   A *The Twenty-one balloons* is about a professor by name William Sherman.

   B "The Twenty-One Balloons" is about a professor, name William Sherman.

   C *The Twenty-One Balloons* is about a professor by the name of William Sherman.

   D Make no change

3 Which sentence does **NOT** belong in paragraph 1?

   A Sentence 2   **C** Sentence 5

   B Sentence 3   **D** Sentence 6

1	Ⓐ	Ⓑ	Ⓒ	Ⓓ
2	Ⓐ	Ⓑ	Ⓒ	Ⓓ
3	Ⓐ	Ⓑ	Ⓒ	Ⓓ

© Macmillan/McGraw-Hill

Reading a Writing Prompt

A writing test requires you to write a composition in response to a prompt. A writing prompt presents a topic for your paper. Look for key words and phrases in the prompt that tell you what you should write about.

Next, determine what you want to say and your purpose for writing. Your purpose may be to explain, describe, entertain, or express your ideas about the topic. Your purpose for writing should help you organize your ideas and help you relate the message to your audience.

Here is an example of a writing prompt:

> **Write a composition about your favorite sport.**

How to Read a Prompt

Identify the Topic: Read the prompt again carefully. The words "your favorite sport" tell you that you will be writing about a sport you enjoy playing or watching.

Identify the Audience: Determine who you want your audience to be. You may want to think of your teacher as your audience.

Choose a Plan for Organizing: You will need to consider how to organize your writing and what kind of writing to produce. Sometimes one prompt can be approached in different ways.

- You could use the prompt above to write a composition that expresses your ideas and feelings about your favorite sport.

- You could use the prompt to write a composition that explains and describes the rules of your favorite sport.

- You could use the prompt to write a composition that entertains your readers by telling about funny things that happen to you when you play your favorite sport.

It's up to you to choose a plan for organizing your writing based on your purpose for writing. Your purpose will help you know how to organize your ideas.

Writing to the Prompt

Here are some tips to remember when you are given a prompt in a writing test:

Before Writing

- Think about your writing purpose.
- Keep your audience in mind.
- Brainstorm ideas about the topic.
- Choose your strongest ideas to include in your writing.
- Focus or narrow the ideas to allow for detail and development of your writer's "voice."

During Writing

- Start with an interesting topic sentence.
- Be sure to put your ideas in logical order.
- Connect ideas with time-order words. Use clear sequence words or phrases to connect thoughts.
- End with a strong conclusion. Don't leave the reader hanging.

After Writing

- Proofread your work. Check that you have followed the rules of capitalization, punctuation, and penmanship to communicate clearly.
- Reorder ideas to make the message clear.
- Omit any statements that repeat ideas or that are not focused on the topic.
- Correct any run-on sentences or sentence fragments.
- Check for spelling errors.
- Begin a new paragraph when needed.

When you read a writing prompt, look for words and phrases that give you ideas. Make a plan and decide how to organize your ideas in the most effective way to communicate your purpose for writing to your audience.

Practice
Exercises

Name_____ Date_____

REVIEW

Setting

The **setting** is where and when a story takes place. Sometimes, the setting is not stated, but you can find clues about it. Look for words that describe the place or the time in history.

Read the selection. Then answer the questions that follow.

A Special Time and Place

Logs crackled in the fireplace. The fire warmed the room, even though snow was falling outside. Mama stirred the kettle that hung over the low flame. The bubbling stew smelled wonderful.

I hurried to set the table. The sun was setting, and that meant Papa would be returning soon. He had taken the horse and buggy into town to buy supplies. We needed kerosene for our lanterns. We also needed coffee and honey. Papa loved honey on his buttermilk biscuits. After his long journey from town, he was sure to be hungry.

1 When do you think the story is set? What clues tell you this?

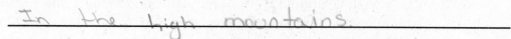
In the high mountains

2 What time of year do you think it is? How do you know?

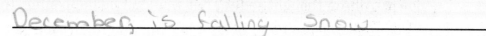
December is falling snow

3 In what part of the house do you think the story is set?

At the back.

How characters dress and speak and the work they do can help you determine where the story takes place.

© Macmillan/McGraw-Hill

Name __Emilio Cáceres__ Date __12-15-09__

PRACTICE

Setting

Read the selection. Then read each question that follows. Mark the letter for that answer.

Allison's Big Surprise

1   As far back as she could remember, Allison dreamed of being a famous singer. When she was six years old, Allison started organizing musical shows starring all of her friends. Of course, she always took the lead role. Back then, it was easy being a star. She was singing in her own backyard with her friends and family gathered around her.

2   Things were different this time. The whole school would be watching Allison. She wasn't just nervous. She was terrified. Allison couldn't remember the last time her stomach had been tied up in such knots. "This must be what they call stage fright," Allison thought to herself.

3   "I wish Grandma were here," Allison sighed as she waited to be announced. Grandma Jenson was like a good luck charm for Allison. Whenever she was nearby, Allison would automatically relax. "If Grandma were in the audience, I just know I would calm down," Allison thought sadly. That wouldn't be happening, though.

4   Grandma Jenson had broken her hip and hadn't left her house in weeks. Allison had gone to visit her almost every day. Grandma's kitchen usually was filled with wonderful smells and delicious treats. The sink would be full of pots and pans that needed scrubbing. Since Grandma's fall, the kitchen had been spotless. The counters had been bare.

5   Allison stared out at the darkness. This room held pleasant memories for her. This is where she would go every school day at noon. This is where she had met her best friend, Carla, last September. Carla had been sitting alone, while kids at nearby tables were chattering away happily. Now, Allison could barely see the tables pushed back along the walls, though she could still smell the pizza from Friday's lunch.

© Macmillan/McGraw-Hill

Name_____ Date_____

6   Thinking about food made Allison's stomach growl. Her mother had prepared her favorite meal for supper, but Allison hadn't felt like eating. Then, before she knew it, the table had been cleared, and her parents were scrambling to get ready. Allison's younger sister was whining about having to wear boots. Allison's brother ran off to throw a few snowballs at his friends down the street, and Allison had to go back for the sheet music she needed. It was a miracle that she had gotten to school on time.

7   Suddenly, Allison heard her name. The audience began to clap as she walked over to the microphone. "I sure hope I remember the words," Allison worried just as the music started to play. She had been practicing her song for weeks, though—in the shower, in the basement, at her grandmother's house. In a flash, Allison remembered how her grandmother's eyes had shone with pride. That memory filled Allison with courage, and she began to sing her heart out.

8   Soon, the room was filled with clapping. "More! More," shouted members of the audience. They all wanted to hear another song! Allison felt herself blush as she took a bow.

9   Finally, the noise died down, and Allison started to leave the stage. The announcer introduced the next performer. Then, out of the corner of her eye, Allison saw her teacher. Mrs. Rodriguez was waving at her, trying to get her attention. Allison hurried down the steps to see what she wanted.

10   "There's someone here who wants your autograph," Mrs. Rodriguez said with a smile. There, sitting in the wheelchair she had borrowed for the night and wearing the woolen scarf Allison had just given her for Christmas, was Grandma Jenson. "Nothing could have kept me from your first performance," her grandmother said.

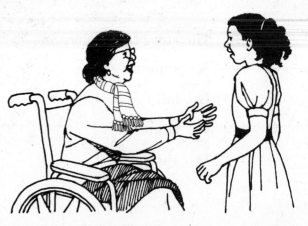

11   Allison hugged her grandmother tightly. "It's almost as if my wishes brought you to me, Grandma," she finally said. "I couldn't have done this without you."

Name_____ **Date**_____

1 Where does the story take place?

   A Allison's backyard

   B The school cafeteria

   C Grandma Jenson's kitchen

   D The school playground

2 What clues help you know where the story takes place?

   A There are tables along the walls, and the room smells like pizza.

   B The room was filled with loud clapping.

   C Allison's teacher smiled at her.

   D Allison's grandmother came to see the performance.

3 The story takes place in—

   A summer

   B fall

   C winter

   D spring

4 What clues help you know what season it is?

   A Scarves, boots, and snowballs are mentioned.

   B Allison was nervous about her first public performance.

   C The audience applauded, and Allison's teacher smiled at her after she finished singing.

   D The room was dark and smelled like pizza.

5 At what time of day does the story take place?

   A In the morning

   B Before lunch

   C In the afternoon

   D In the evening

6 What is the weather like on the day of the performance?

   A It is warm and sunny.

   B It is cold and snowy.

   C It is hot and dry.

   D It is dark and raining.

Name_____ **Date**_____

7 Which of these best describes how Allison feels at the beginning of the passage?

   A Really nervous

   B Happy to see her grandmother

   C Very hungry

   D Worried about Carla

8 What kind of performance is taking place?

   A A class play

   B A band practice

   C A talent show

   D A science fair

9 From what the reader learns about Grandma Jenson, which statement would not be reasonable?

   A Grandma Jenson is very close to Allison.

   B Grandma Jenson is a good cook.

   C Grandma Jenson has not left home much recently.

   D Grandma Jenson does not enjoy music.

10 Which of these best describes the scene as Allison's family prepared to leave the house?

   A It was calm and relaxed.

   B It was hectic and rushed.

   C It was very cold.

   D Everyone was full after dinner.

Name_____ Date_____

REVIEW

Supporting a Central Idea

The **central idea** tells what a piece of writing is about.
Supporting details help to clarify or develop the central idea.

When revising, reread your writing to make sure that your ideas
and details are connected. Delete any details that do not support the
central idea. See if adding words such as *next* and *then* will make
your ideas seem more connected.

Read the paragraph. Then answer the questions that follow.

Spring

    In my opinion, spring is the nicest time of year. The weather is
neither too hot nor too cold. Colorful flowers bloom in yards and
along roadways. Trees are dressed in fresh green leaves, and baby
birds chirp in their nests. Everyone I know seems happy to be
outdoors. In the fall, the leaves turn beautiful shades of red and
gold.

1   What is the central idea of this paragraph?

    How spring is the nicest time.

2   List in order details that support this idea.

    The weather is neither too hot nor to cold.

    Colorful flowers bloom in yards and along

    roadways

3   Which detail should be removed from the paragraph?

    In the fall, the leaves turn beutifulshades

You may find the central idea of a story stated in the title
or in a topic sentence near the beginning.

© Macmillan/McGraw-Hill

Name Emilio Cá   Date _____

PRACTICE

Supporting a Central Idea

Franklin is in the fourth grade and sometimes writes stories in his free time. He is writing a story about his cousin Jake. Read Franklin's story and look for corrections or improvements he could make. Then answer the multiple-choice questions that follow.

Adventures at Rivercrest State Park

(1) Jake's family spent last weekend at Rivercrest State Park. (2) On Saturday morning, they went swimming. (3) Jake's friend Lucy wants to be a lifeguard one day. (4) Then they took a ride around the park on a small train with open passenger cars. (5) Jake waved at everyone he passed. (6) After the train ride, Jake's family had a delicious picnic lunch. (7) Next the family went to the playground, where they stayed the rest of the afternoon.

(8) Saturday evening at Rivercrest State Park was an adventure. (9) Jake and his brother went off to collect firewood. (10) Jake's brother picked up an old log, only to find a small snake curled up beneath it. (11) Snakes usually sheds their skins at least once a year. (12) After the snake slithered away, Jake and his brother set off to find more wood.

Name_____ **Date**_____

#7   (13) They found a pile of broken limbs. (14) They started to cut the branches off. (15) Soon they noticed a slight odor coming from the woodpile. (16) Jake moved a few branches and then jumped back in surprise. (17) There, under the branches, lay a small skunk! (18) Jake and his brother dashed back to their cabin by the river. (19) "We don't really need a campfire tonight," Jake said with a grin.

© Macmillan/McGraw-Hill

Name_____ **Date**_____

1 Which sentence states the central idea of the first paragraph?

A Sentence 1 *? Yes is central Idiea*

B Sentence 2 *X Is not that*

C Sentence 4 *X No is not that one*

D Sentence 8 *X No is not that P.1*

2 Each of these words helps connect sentences in the first paragraph except—

A *Then* *X It correct*

B *waved* *? Doesn't connect*

C *After* *X Theiy conect*

D *Next* *X It conect*

3 Which sentence does **NOT** belong in the first paragraph?

A Sentence 2 *X It belongs*

B Sentence 3 *? Doesn belong*

C Sentence 4 *X It belong*

D Sentence 6 *X It belong*

4 Which sentence could **BEST** be added after sentence 7?

A Jake's school has a nice playground. *X Is not that*

B Jake's mother ate a turkey and cheese sandwich, and Jake ate some watermelon. *X No doesn't matter*

C "This has been a great day so far!" said Jake as he rested on the swings. *? It could be*

D The temperature was 86 degrees that day. *X No is not that S.7*

5 Which sentence states the central idea of the second paragraph?

A Sentence 8 *? It could be*

B Sentence 9 *X Is not that*

C Sentence 11 *X Is not that one*

D Sentence 12 *X No is not the central idea P.2*

6 What change, if any, should be made in sentence 11?

A Change *their* to *there* *X No is not that*

B Change *Snakes* to *Snaiks* *X Mis spell*

C Change *sheds* to *shed* *? It could be*

D Make no change *X*

S.11

© Macmillan/McGraw-Hill

Name_____ Date_____

7 What is the **BEST** way to combine sentences 13 and 14?

   A They found a pile of broken limbs, they started to cut the branches off. ✗ No

is not that

   B They found a pile of broken limbs, but then they started to cut the branches off. ✗ Need

and

   C They found a pile of broken limbs and started to cut the branches off. ? It could

be

   D They found a pile of broken limbs with branches cut off. ✗

S.13 & 14 No it doesn't say that

8 Which sentence could **BEST** be added after sentence 19?

   A Campfires should always be watched carefully and kept under control. ✗ Is not

that

   B Skunks can be dangerous if they are frightened. ✗ Is

not that ✗ Is

   C Even without a campfire, spending the night in the cabin by the river was cozy. ?

It could be?

   D Some campgrounds do not allow campers to gather firewood for campfires. ✗

no is not that is not

S.14

9 Which of these sentences **BEST** states a central idea for a fourth paragraph?

   A Sunday started out with a bang for Jake and his family. ?

   B Jake's favorite subject at school is science. ✗

   C Jake's dad usually works on the weekend. ✗

   D Jake is one year older than his brother, but his brother is two inches taller. ✗

10 Which of the following would be another good title for this story?

   A Lunch at the Picnic Grounds ✗

   B Family Fun at the Park ?

   C The Train to Nowhere ✗

   D Escape from a Skunk ✗

Name_____ **Date**_____

 # WRITE

> Write a composition about your favorite outdoor activity.

The box below will help you write your composition. Then, on another piece of paper write your composition.

REMEMBER TO—

- ❏ write about your favorite outdoor activity

- ❏ make sure that each sentence you write tells about the outdoor activity

- ❏ support your ideas with details so that the reader really understands what you are saying ....

- ❏ check for correct spelling, capitalization, punctuation, grammar, and sentences

Supporting details help develop the central idea.

Name_____ Date_____

REVIEW

Understanding Character

Some questions ask you to figure out how a character feels. Look for clues that describe a character's actions or words. For example, if a character is yawning a lot, then you might say the character feels tired.

Read the paragraph. Then answer the questions that follow.

A Moving Experience

Jacey wiped the tears from her cheeks as she looked around the room one last time. All her things were packed. Soon the movers would be here. They would load all her family's possessions into a big van. Tomorrow, Jacey would be moving into a new house in the city.

1   How do you think Jacey is feeling?

Sad cause she is moving

2   What clue does the author give to help you know this?

Packed all her things

3   Did your own experiences or knowledge help you understand Jacey's feelings? If so, how?

_No._

_____

Sometimes, you can make inferences about a character based on a picture that goes with a story.

Name_____ Date_____

PRACTICE

Understanding Character

Read the selection. Then read each question that follows. Decide which is the best answer. Mark the letter for that answer.

Tran's First Day

1   Tran's heart was pounding, and his hands were shaking. It was his first day at a new school. Tran's family moved from city to city because of his father's job. It was always the same. Tran would make friends and start to feel comfortable in his new room in his new home. Then it would be time to go. Again. "I'm so tired of being 'the new kid' everywhere I go," Tran thought to himself as his mouth settled into a frown.

2   Last night, Tran had complained to his dad about moving. Mr. Lee had listened patiently, nodding his head as Tran listed his fears. "I know starting over is difficult, son," Mr. Lee said. "But try to think of a move as an exciting adventure. You get the chance to meet interesting people. You get the chance to travel cross-country and see interesting places." Tran wasn't convinced. Given the choice, he would have picked "boring and familiar" over "interesting and new" anytime.

3   "Here we go again," Tran grumbled bitterly as he passed through the school gates. He managed to drag himself as far as the main stairway and then stopped. His feet felt like lead, and, to make matters worse, his stomach was churning. He had not eaten breakfast that morning. In fact, he couldn't imagine eating ever again. "Just get me to the classroom at the end of the hall," Tran silently begged his reluctant body. He didn't want to make a scene. He just wanted to be invisible.

4   When he reached the classroom, Tran spotted an empty seat right near the back. He nabbed it and was very satisfied with the location. Maybe no one would notice him over there. He got settled and then suddenly became aware of all of the noise around him. There were students talking about their summer vacations. There were students talking about their plans for the school year.

Name_____ Date_____

Actually, there was a lot of talking going on, but nobody was talking to HIM! Tran felt himself squirm with discomfort.

5   After a few moments, a boy that everyone seemed to know walked into the room. Several students called out to him as he entered, and he smiled happily and waved to his classmates. The boy looked around for an empty seat and took the first one he spotted. It was right next to Tran.

6   "Hi. My name is Matt," the boy said. "I haven't seen you around before. Are you new?" he asked. Tran felt like yelling angrily, "I'm *always* new," but instead, he shyly mentioned that he had just moved to town. "Well, you'll like it here at Center Street School," Matt said brightly. Tran wasn't so sure.

7   Tran didn't know what to say next, so there was an awkward silence. For the first time, Matt noticed how sad Tran's face looked. He tried to imagine how it must feel to start at a new school in a new town. After a moment, Matt had an idea. "Our class always plays kickball at recess. Would you like to be on my team?" he asked Tran.

8   Tran didn't have to think twice about the offer. Kickball was his specialty. He had been a star player at his last school. "That sounds great!" Tran replied, smiling broadly. Just then the teacher called the class to order. As Tran took out his books, he began counting the minutes until recess. He also began wondering about lunch. All of a sudden, Tran realized that he had developed quite an appetite!

Name_____ Date_____

1 Which of these best describes how Tran feels at the start of the selection?

A Happy

B Nervous and scared

C Grateful

D Silly

2 Which is the best clue that the author gives to show how Tran feels at the beginning of the story?

A He moved from city to city.

B He gets to see interesting places.

C His heart was pounding, and his hands were shaking.

D He didn't like walking to school.

3 Which of these best descirbes how Tran feels when Matt invites him to play kickball?

A Happy

B Shy

C Rested

D Anxious

4 Which clue best helps the reader figure out how Tran feels after Matt asks him to play?

A He takes out his school books.

B He remembers playing kickball at his old school.

C He waits for the teacher to call the class to order.

D He answers Matt excitedly and smiles broadly.

5 Which of these best describes Matt?

A Popular and friendly

B Proud

C Embarrassed

D Impatient

6 What will most likely happen during recess?

A The captain of the other team will want Tran to play for him.

B Tran will join Matt's kickball team.

C Matt and Tran will use the time to finish some schoolwork.

D Tran will not eat.

Name_____ **Date**_____

7 Why do you think Matt asks Tran to join the kickball team?

   A He needs an extra player.

   B He wants Tran to get exercise.

   C He heard that Tran was a star player at his last school.

   (D) He wants to help Tran feel part of the class.

8 What does Tran do first after he reaches the classroom?

   (A) He listens to students talk about their summer vacations.

   B He thinks about playing kickball during recess.

   C He chooses a seat in the back.

   D He starts talking to Matt.

9 Tran develops an appetite at the end of the story because—

   A he hears the food in the school cafeteria is tasty

   B he feels more relaxed and happier about his new school

   C he wants to have energy to play kickball

   (D) he had skipped breakfast because he was in a rush

10 Why do Tran's feelings change at the end of the story?

   A He thinks about what his father said the night before.

   B He is happy to feel hungry once again.

   C Matt realizes that Tran is good at playing kickball.

   (D) He feels like Matt will be his friend and he won't feel lonely.

© Macmillan/McGraw-Hill

Name _Emilio Caceres_ Date _12-06-10_

REVIEW

Staying on Topic

When you choose a topic for writing, you must first decide which details to include. Then you organize these details into paragraphs.

Read the passage below. Then answer the questions that follow.

Marvin the Hamster Is Missing!

I have always wanted a pet hamster. My parents gave me one a few weeks ago. I named my hamster Marvin, after my uncle. My uncle has a farm in Oklahoma.

Less than two weeks after I got Marvin, a terrible thing happened. Marvin disappeared. Somehow he escaped from his cage. I noticed that he was gone when I went to feed him. I was very upset.

Dad helped me look all over the house for Marvin. We checked under the furniture. We looked behind the refrigerator and the stove. We even checked around the outside of the house.

1 What is the topic of this passage?

    Marvin the hamster is missing.

2 Which detail could you add that supports the topic? Circle the letter.

    A   Hamsters make good pets. X

    (B) Mom joined in the search, too. ?

    C   I feed Marvin seeds and hamster food. X

    D   Our house is surrounded by a fence. X

3 Which detail should be removed because it does not relate to the topic?

    My uncle has a form on okkhoma

Name _Emilio C._   Date _10-06-16_

PRACTICE

Staying on Topic

Lily is writing a report for school. Read Lily's report and think about ways it can be improved. Answer the questions that follow Lily's report.

An Unusual Animal

(1) Madagascar is an island off the east coast of Africa. (2) It is home to many strange and beautiful creatures. (3) Lemurs is among the most unusual animals found on Madagascar. (4) Some are as small as mice. (5) This island is the only place on Earth where lemurs live in the wild. (6) Around 30 different species of lemurs live on Madagascar.

(7) Some lemurs are the size of house cats. (8) Others, like the sifaka lemur, are even bigger. (9) But all lemurs have the same striking feature. (10) Lemurs have large eyes that allow them to see in the dark. (11) This is helpful for the lemur species that are active at night. (12) Many lemurs eat coconuts, too.

(13) Lemurs are great tree climbers. (14) Lemurs are great jumpers. (15) The sifaka lemur can jump as far as 20 feet! (16) The lemur leaps from tree to tree looking for food. (17) Sifaka lemurs have a different jumping technique than most other lemurs. (18) After they jump, they land feet first. (19) Most lemurs land hands first, like monkeys.

© Macmillan/McGraw-Hill

Name_____Emilio_____ Date_1-06-80_

(20) The trees of Madagascar provide a variety of food for lemurs. (21) Some lemurs, like the sifaka, prefer fruit and leaves. (22) Aye-aye lemurs hunt for bugs and grubs. (23) Their idea of a tasty meal!

1 What is the central idea of the first paragraph?

   A Only strange animals live on Madagascar.

   B Madagascar is an island off the east coast of Africa.

   C Madagascar is home to the world's lemurs.

   D Lemurs only live in the wild.

2 What change, if any, should be made in sentence 3?

   A Change *unusual* to **usual**

   B Change *Madagascar* to **madagascar**

   C Change *is* to **are**

   D Make no change

Name_____ Date_____

3 Which sentence does **NOT** belong in the first paragraph?

   A Sentence 1

   B Sentence 2

   C Sentence 4

   D Sentence 5

4 What is the central idea of the second paragraph?

   A All lemurs have the same striking feature.

   B Some lemurs are only as big as cats.

   C Lemurs move about at night.

   D Lemurs can see in the dark.

5 Which sentence does **NOT** belong in the second paragraph?

   A Sentence 7

   B Sentence 8

   C Sentence 10

   D Sentence 12

6 Which sentence could **BEST** be added before sentence 7?

   A Lemurs come in all different sizes.

   B Lemurs are more intelligent than dogs.

   C Like people, lemurs live in families.

   D A new lemur species was recently discovered.

7 What is the **BEST** way to combine sentences 13 and 14?

   A Lemurs are great tree climbers and jumpers.

   B Lemurs are great tree climbers, and jumpers.

   C Lemurs are great, tree climbers and jumpers.

   D Lemurs are great tree-climber jumpers.

Name_____ Date_____

8 Which of the following is **NOT** a complete sentence?

   A Sentence 2

   B Sentence 14

   C Sentence 22

   D Sentence 23

9 Which of the following would make a good topic sentence for a fifth paragraph?

   A The rain forest is filled with many kinds of plants.

   B Madagascar is a beautiful island.

   C Unfortunately, the lemurs' habitat is in danger.

   D Lemurs like to hide from people.

10 Another good title for this selection would be—

   A African Rain Forests

   B The Lemurs of Madagascar

   C Lemurs Are Smarter Than You Think

   D Lunchtime for Lemurs

Name_____ **Date**_____

WRITE

> Write a composition about how you and a family member are alike or different.

The box below will help you write your composition. Then, on another piece of paper write your composition.

REMEMBER TO—

❏ write at least two paragraphs about a friend or family member

❏ make sure that each paragraph you write helps the reader understand how you and your friend or family member are alike and different

❏ be sure all the sentences you write relate to your topic ·····················

❏ use correct spelling, capitalization, punctuation, grammar, and sentences

Does any paragraph contain details that do not relate to your topic?

Name Emilio Cáceres   **Date** 10/14/09

REVIEW

Multiple-Meaning Words

Many words have **multiple meanings**. You can use clues within the sentence to decide which meaning is the correct one.

Read the sentence. Pay attention to the underlined word.

The birds pulled strips of <u>bark</u> from the tree to make their nest.

1   In this sentence, what does the word <u>bark</u> mean? Circle the letter.
    A   The noise a dog makes ✗
    B   The outer part of a tree ?
    C   To give an order ✗
    D   To speak loudly and sharply ✗

The word <u>tree</u> is a clue; also, birds do not use the noise a dog makes to build a nest.

Read the sentence. Then answer the questions that follow.

I woke up this morning when I heard the rooster crow.

2   In this sentence, what does the word <u>crow</u> mean? Circle the letter.
    A   The loud cry of a rooster ?
    B   A large black bird ✗
    C   To boast in triumph ✗
    D   A Native American tribe ✗

3   What clues helped you decide on the correct meaning?

The clues that help me decide were the

words heard the rooster.

TEST-TAKING TIP   Some multiple-meaning words are pronounced differently, depending on which meaning is used.

© Macmillan/McGraw-Hill

Name Emilio Caceres   Date 14/14/09

PRACTICE

(handwritten) How
#2 Nick and logan felt abou the line at the ride.
#4 what Nick and logan do after they buy cotton candy.

Multiple-Meaning Words

Read the two selections. Then read each question that follows. Decide which is the best answer. Mark the letter for that answer.

Roller Coaster's Revenge

1   Nick and Logan were bursting with excitement. This was the first day of summer vacation, and they had big plans. Last night, Mom and Dad had given them permission to bike all the way down to Chester Street. The boys had promised to be careful and to obey the light at the corner. Now, they were headed for the fair.

2   This was the first time that the county fair was being held in their town. There were games to play, contests to enter, and exhibits to visit. Best of all, there were all kinds of thrilling rides to try. There were bumper cars, a Ferris wheel, and an enormous roller coaster. For Nick and Logan, that was the main attraction. They parked their bikes and bought their tickets.

3   "I want to ride the roller coaster first!" said Nick excitedly. "Come on," he said, tugging at his brother's shirt impatiently.

4   "Just wait," suggested Logan. "Do you see that line? It looks like the whole town had that same idea. Let's get some cotton candy. We can eat it while we wait our turn," he continued.

5   To the left of the roller coaster was a group of food vendors. The boys rushed over to get some cotton candy and then raced back. They stood at the base of the roller coaster and looked up. "Wow! I didn't realize how high the roller coaster was!" exclaimed Nick.

6   "And look how fast it goes down that steep hill!" added Logan. Then he turned his attention back to the sweet treat in his hand. "You know," he began after a while, "maybe getting this cotton candy wasn't the greatest idea after all. I know what goes up must come down," continued Logan. "But this time, I'm afraid what goes down might come up!"

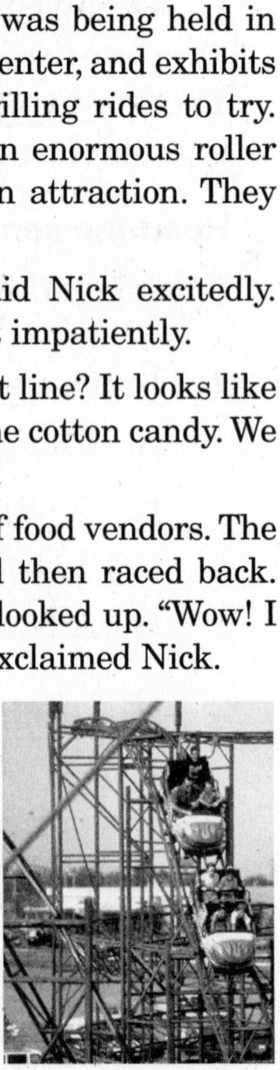

Name Emilio   **Date** 10-14-09

The Missing Music

1   At long last, Josie reached the final note of the waltz she had been playing. After her first ten mistakes, she had simply stopped counting. She knew she had to turn around and bow to the judges. She wouldn't let them see her tears, but she couldn't erase the frown from her face.

2   "I can't help it that I lost my music," she blurted out to her teacher as she left the stage. "It's not fair that they made me play the waltz without it," she continued grumpily.

3   "You are responsible for your own music, Josie. You know that," said her teacher gently. "I guess next time you'll be more careful with your sheet music."

4   Josie headed gloomily back to her classroom to grab her coat and her backpack. When she got there, she noticed a few stray pieces of paper on the floor. Josie bent down to pick them up and toss them into the trash can. As she rose up, though, she glimpsed rows of musical notes on the top sheet.

5   "My missing music," she gasped. "It was here all the time! It must have slipped out of my backpack when I was rushing to get ready. Next time I'll be more careful where I put it," Josie promised herself. "Thank goodness I was careful enough not to throw it away!"

#6 Setting   #7 How Joise felts after her performence

#5
#10

#8

Name_____ Date_____

Use "Roller Coaster's Revenge" (p. 36) to answer questions 1–4.

1 In paragraph 4, the word <u>turn</u> means—

    A a change of direction

    B an opportunity

    C to twist around

    D to become spoiled or sour

2 Which of these best describes how Nick and Logan felt when they saw the line at the roller coaster?

    A Disappointed

    B Nervous

    C Happy

    D Confused

3 In paragraph 5, the word <u>left</u> means—

    A departed

    B the opposite of *right*

    C the last one remaining

    D on the side

4 What did Nick and Logan do after they bought cotton candy?

    A They joined the line for the roller coaster.

    B They parked their bikes.

    C They met some friends.

    D They joined the line for the bumper cars.

Use "The Missing Music" (p. 37) to answer questions 5–8.

5 In paragraph 2, the word <u>left</u> means—

    A on the side

    B the last one remaining

    C the opposite of *right*

    D departed

6 Where does this selection take place?

    A In a school auditorium

    B In a schoolyard

    C At a town concert hall

    D At the music teacher's house

Name_____ Date_____

7 Which of these best describes how Josie felt after her performance?

   A Disappointed

   B Proud

   C Shy

   D Nervous

8 In paragraph 4, the word <u>rose</u> means—

   A a type of flower

   B a deep pink color

   C increased in price

   D stood up

Use "Roller Coaster's Revenge," "The Missing Music," and the dictionary entries below to answer questions 9–10.

> **fair** (fâr)
> *adj.* **1.** according to rules. *The judge made a fair decision.* **2.** bright and sunny; not cloudy. *They predicted fair weather for the weekend.* **3.** light in coloring. *The girl had fair skin.*
> *n.* **4.** a festival or exhibition.

9 Which definition of <u>fair</u> is used in paragraph 1 of "Roller Coaster's Revenge"?

   A Meaning 1

   B Meaning 2

   C Meaning 3

   D Meaning 4

10 Which definition of <u>fair</u> is used in paragraph 2 of "The Missing Music"?

   A Meaning 1

   B Meaning 2

   C Meaning 3

   D Meaning 4

© Macmillan/McGraw-Hill

Name _Emilio Cáceres_   Date _10-15-9_

REVIEW

Combining Sentences

There are several ways to **combine sentences** to make them less repetitive. One way is to combine subjects using *and* to form a **compound subject**.

Liam saw the shaggy dog. I saw the shaggy dog.

Improved: Liam **and** I saw the shaggy dog.

Another way is to combine predicates using *and* to form a **compound predicate**.

Antoine likes to bake cookies. Antoine likes to eat cookies.

Improved: Antoine likes to bake *and* eat cookies.

Short, choppy sentences can also be combined to form **compound sentences**. Use conjunctions such as *and* and *but* to combine sentences.

The students went to the science museum. They didn't see the dinosaur exhibit.

Improved: The students went to the science museum, **but** they didn't see the dinosaur exhibit.

Combine each pair of sentences into one sentence.

1   My brother acted in a movie. I acted in a movie.

My brother and I acted in a movie.

2   Zach rode the roller coaster. Zach rode the Ferris wheel.

Zach rode the roller coaster and the Ferris wheels.

3   The neighbors heard a loud noise. They saw a bright flash.

The neighbors heard a loud noise and saw a bright flash.

Name Emilio Cáceres   **Date** 10-15-09

PRACTICE

Combining Sentences

Jenny is writing a mystery story for a class assignment. Read her story and consider improvements you think Jenny might make. When you are finished reading, answer the questions that follow.

A women.

A man tha has a darkk jacket and a hat

The Strangest Stranger

(1) I took my first train trip alone in 2001. (2) The only train I could take left at night. (3) My mother was upset. (4) I told her not to worry. (5) I would probably sleep soundly. (6) I would probably sleep for the whole trip.

(7) There was only one other person in my train car. (8) She was wearing a hat and a scarf that covered everything but her eyes. (9) Sometime during the night, the woman walked down the aisle and sat in the seat opposite me. (10) She pulled out a pair of scissors. (11) She placed the scissors on the seat. (12) She peered at me with her beady eyes. (13) I turned off the overhead light. (14) I pretended to fall asleep.

(15) "Turn that back on!" snapped the woman. (16) I did as she said. (17) "Are you afraid of me?" she asked.

(18) "No," I said as confidently as I could manage. (19) I tried not to let my voice shake.

(20) "Take these," she commanded as she handed me the scissors.

(21) "You are going to cut my hair."

© Macmillan/McGraw-Hill

Name_____ Date_____

(22) "I don't know how!" I exclaimed.

(23) "Be quiet," the woman said. (24) "I'll tell you how to cut it," the woman said. (25) She took off her hat. (26) Her long red locks fell almost to her waist. (27) She guided my hand as I cut off most of her hair.

(28) "You must do one more thing for me," she whispered in my ear. (29) "Turn and look out the window." (30) I looked out the window. (31) I looked for what seemed like hours. (32) All I could hear was a rustling in the seat next to me.

(33) Finally, the train pulled into the next station. (34) The woman sitting opposite me had disappeared and in her place sat a train conductor. (35) The conductor had her cap pulled way down so you could hardly see her face. (36) The train conductor stood up. (37) I stood up. (38) The train conductor began to walk down the aisle towards the back of the train. (39) Just then, a police officer entered the car quickly, passed the train conductor, and asked me if I had seen a woman with long red hair. (40) The police officer wore a blue shirt. (41) I was shocked. (42) I didn't know what to say. (43) I don't think they never found that mysterious redheaded stranger.

© Macmillan/McGraw-Hill

Name_____ Date_____

1   What is the **BEST** way to combine sentences 3 and 4?

   A   My mother was upset I told her not to worry.

   B   My mother was upset because I told her not to worry.

   C   My mother was upset, but I told her not to worry.

   D   My mother and I were upset.

2   Which other two sentences in the first paragraph should be combined?

   A   Sentences 1 and 2

   B   Sentences 5 and 6

   C   Sentences 2 and 3

   D   Sentences 1 and 3

3   Which sentence does **NOT** belong in this story?

   A   Sentence 7

   B   Sentence 21

   C   Sentence 34

   D   Sentence 40

4   What is the **BEST** way to combine sentences 13 and 14?

   A   I turned off the overhead light and pretended to fall asleep.

   B   I turned off the overhead light I pretended to fall asleep.

   C   I pretended to fall asleep and turned off the overhead light.

   D   I turned off the overhead light, but I pretended to fall asleep.

5   What is the **BEST** way to combine sentences 23 and 24?

   A   "Be quiet I'll tell you how you cut it," the woman said.

   B   "I'll tell you how to cut it be quiet," the woman said.

   C   "Be quiet, and I'll tell you how to cut it," the woman said.

   D   "Be quiet, but I'll tell you how to cut it," the woman said.

Name_____ Date_____

6 What is the **BEST** way to combine sentences 30 and 31?

    A I looked out the window, I looked for what seemed like hours.

    B I looked out the window for three hours.

    C I looked out the window for what seemed like hours.

    D I looked for hours.

7 Which sentence could **BEST** be added after sentence 32?

    A I had always enjoyed train rides before.

    B I was wearing a new dress.

    C I had forgotten my watch.

    D What was she doing?

8 What is the **BEST** way to combine sentences 36 and 37?

    A The train conductor stood up and I stood up.

    B I and the train conductor stood up.

    C The train conductor and I stood up.

    D She stood and I stood.

9 What is the **BEST** way to combine sentences 41 and 42?

    A I was shocked and didn't know what to say.

    B I was so shocked and so I didn't know what to say.

    C I didn't know what to say, I was that shocked!

    D I was shocked, I didn't know what to say.

10 What change, if any, should be made in sentence 43?

    A Change *don't* to **dont**

    B Change *never* to **ever**

    C Change *found* to **find**

    D Make no change

Name_____ **Date**_____

WRITE

Write about your favorite television show or book.

The box below will help you write your composition. Then, on another piece of paper write your composition.

REMEMBER TO—

❑ write about your favorite television program or book

❑ make sure that you express your views clearly and that your ideas flow in a ⋯⋯⋯ logical order

❑ include details to help the reader understand what you are saying and descriptive words to communicate what the show is about and why you enjoy it so much

❑ check your spelling, capitalization, punctuation, and grammar carefully

Combining sentences can help your writing flow more smoothly.

Name Emilio Cáceres   **Date** 10-22-09

REVIEW

Problem and Resolution

A story often has a **problem** as its main focus. A character must find an answer, or **resolution**, to the problem.

Read the selection. Then answer the questions that follow.

A Mouthful of Problems

As you know, George Washington was the first President of the United States. Did you know, though, that he had trouble with his teeth? Over the years, he had one toothache after another. Back in those days, when a person's tooth hurt, the dentist simply pulled it. After a while, Washington had no teeth at all. This made eating difficult, so Washington had to order false teeth. His false teeth were made for him from cow's teeth and hippopotamus ivory. They were held in his mouth with metal springs.

1   What problem did George Washington have over the years?

George washigton had one tooth after another.

2   Who helped him solve his problem?

The dentist was the person who helped solve George washington.

3   What was the resolution?

The dentist simply pulled the teeth.

4   What new problem did this resolution cause?

George washigton didn't have any teeth left.

5   How did George Washington solve this new problem?

George Washigton solved his new problem by ordering false teeth.

The main problem in a story or article is often described in the first few paragraphs.

Name Emilio Cáceres   **Date** 10-22-09

#1 Where Noora & Ahmed lived.

#2 Noora's description

PRACTICE

#3 Childrens concern over the cat.

#4 Ahmed & Noora don't think the cat is not straight

Problem and Resolution

#5 What Problem do Ahmed and Noora face finding a shelter.

#6 what problem face in kipping Mister

Read the selection. Then read each question that follows the selection. Decide which is the best answer to each question. Mark the letter for that answer.

#7 when Mothers attitude change

Mixer

Mashine Person Animal name

#10 what is shown with Noora & Ahmed making posters

1   I'm really glad I have a big sister. Sometimes Noora's a pain, but sometimes she's really great. For instance, last summer when we found a stray cat wandering down our street, Noora knew just what to do.

2   Our block is often quiet, but since it's a county road, at rush hour it gets pretty busy. At that time of day, cars go zooming down our street as if it were a freeway. So I knew right away that a cat shouldn't be wandering so near the road. And I knew it was a stray because it was awfully muddy. There had been a thunderstorm the night before, and I was pretty sure that the cat had been out in it. Besides, it looked thin and hungry. When it saw us, it ran right up and put its paws on my knees.

3   "Noora, we have to do something. This cat can't stay out here," I said, getting ready for an argument, but no argument came. I ruffled its muddy fur and discovered that underneath all that dirt and grime was black, white, and orange fur. The cat meowed and purred as Noora bent down to pet it, too. We noticed that there wasn't any collar or tag. "Poor no-name cat," I said. "I want to call it Mixer, because its coat has so many colors all mixed up."

4   "Now, Ahmed," Noora replied. "You shouldn't give it a name because we probably won't be able to keep it. You know Mom still misses Kali and doesn't want another pet." Kali was Mom's cat. She was fifteen years old when she died last February. I still missed her a lot, too, but I sure wanted another pet.

5   "Well, we can at least feed it," I pleaded.

6   "That's right," agreed Noora. "And we can try to find it a good home." I picked up the cat and took it into the house. We didn't have

#9 How cat shows it trusts Noora and Ahmed

Name_____ Date_____

cat food anymore, so I looked in the refrigerator for something it might like. I hoped the cat would like chicken, and it did!

7   Noora wanted to know where the cat came from. So, we called local vets. Nobody they knew had lost a black, white, and orange cat. Next we called pet shelters. Most had no room for another cat. One shelter had room but wanted only kittens. Mixer was definitely not a kitten. Although the shelters took our name, their waiting lists were very long.

8   Just as Noora called the last shelter, Mom came rushing in the door from work. She took one look at Mixer and began glaring at the two of us. Noora and I hastened to explain how we'd found the muddy stray.

9   "Don't worry, Mom," I assured her. "We're just feeding it. Then we'll put up posters and try to find its owner or a good home for it."

10   "We've already called lots of shelters," Noora added as Mixer wove in and out of Mom's legs, purring up a storm.

11   As Mom watched Mixer, her face started to soften. "She's so skinny," she said, lifting the cat to get a better look.

12   "We've already fed her the chicken sandwich that was in the refrigerator," said Noora. "How do you know the cat's a she?"

13   "From her coloring," replied Mom. "She's a calico, and calicos are usually female. . . . What if no one wants to take her?" Mom sighed.

14   "Oh, we'll find someone," I boasted. Noora winked at me when Mom wasn't looking, and I nodded back.

15   "I suppose we could keep her," volunteered Mom. "That is, if no one claims her after you put up your posters. Ahmed, bring me Kali's comb and brush, will you?" Then to Mixer she said, "We have to get you cleaned up. Don't we, pretty girl?"

16   And, that's how we got our new cat last summer. Lots of people saw the posters, but no one called to adopt her. Since then, our calico has been eating well and getting lots of attention. She lies on the desk when Noora does her homework. She sits on Mom's lap every evening in the big chair. Then she sleeps with me at night. But I don't call her Mixer anymore. Mom named her Calico.

Name___Emilio Cáceres___ 40   Date 6 - 22 - 09

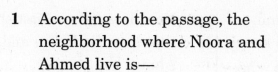
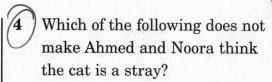

1   According to the passage, the neighborhood where Noora and Ahmed live is—

   P. 2

   A   always quiet ✗
   B   always noisy ✗
   C   on a freeway ✗
   Ⓓ   on a county road ?

2   Which of these best describes Noora?

   A   Curious ✗
   B   Angry ✗   P.3
   Ⓒ   Clever ?
   D   Sad ✗

3   What is the children's first concern when they find the stray cat?

   A   They fear it will get hurt. ✗
   Ⓑ   They have no cat food in the house. ?   P.6
   C   They don't have any way to clean the mud from its fur. ✗
   D   They don't want another cat. ✗

④   Which of the following does not make Ahmed and Noora think the cat is a stray?

   Ⓐ   It has no collar or tag. ?
   B   It is black, white, and orange. ✗
   C   It is thin and hungry. ✗
   D   It is covered with mud. ✗

5   What problem do Noora and Ahmed have in trying to place the cat in a shelter?

   A   Most of the shelters are too far away. ✗
   B   Most of the shelters take only dogs. ✗
   Ⓒ   Most of the shelters are full. ?
   D   Most of the shelters charge a fee. ✗   P.7

Name_____ **Date**_____

6 What problem do Noora and Ahmed face in wanting to keep Mixer?

    A They cannot afford a cat.

    B They have too many pets already.

    C Their mother does not want a new pet.

    D They don't have cat food.

7 Their mother's attitude toward the cat begins to change when—

    A Ahmed offers to do all the work in caring for Mixer

    B the children say they don't plan to keep the cat

    C the children beg her over and over to keep Mixer

    D she sees how much Mixer looks like Kali

8 In paragraph 8, the word hastened means—

    A hurried

    B attached something to something else

    C attempted or tried

    D refused

9 How does the cat first show that it trusts Noora and Ahmed?

    A It eats food in their kitchen.

    B It runs to them and puts its paws on Ahmed's knees.

    C It sleeps on Ahmed's bed.

    D It wanders into their neighborhood.

10 Noora and Ahmed put up posters to see if the cat already had an owner. This showed that they—

    A didn't really want to keep the stray

    B were responsible citizens

    C were talented artists

    D had a lot of spare time

Name Emilio Caceres   **Date** 10-26-09

REVIEW

Capitalization

Certain words in your writing should begin with a capital letter. A word that names a particular person, place, or thing is called a **proper noun**. Proper nouns always begin with a capital letter.

Example: Houston   August   Officer Shipley

The first word in a **title** is always capitalized. Other important words in titles also begin with a capital letter.

Examples: Lost at Sea

The Incredible Voyage to Another Galaxy

My Dog, the World Class Digger

Read the paragraph. Then complete the exercises that follow.

What I did last summer

My family visited the Grand canyon last june. We drove from our home in texas all the way to Arizona. I couldn't wait to get there. What an amazing sight! The canyon was formed by the colorado River. It is more than ten miles wide in some places. We visited a museum there. I learned about the Anasazi. They were the Native americans who first settled in the canyon more than 800 years ago.

1   Draw three lines under each letter that needs to be capitalized in this paragraph, including the title.

2   Write all the proper nouns in the paragraph on the lines below.

Texas, Americans, Summer, Colorado, June, Arizona, Grand Canyon, Native Americans

When you proofread your work, make sure that all proper nouns are capitalized.

Name Emilio Cáceres   **Date** 10-26-9

PRACTICE

100

Capitalization

Maria is writing a letter to her cousin about her summer plans. Read her letter and think about improvements she might make. When you are finished reading, answer the questions that follow.

A Letter from Maria

3413 Lake Street

Seguin, TX 78155

June 25, 2002

Dear Teresa,

(1) How are you? (2) Is it hot in dallas this summer? (3) It's really hot here in seguin. (4) I don't think it's been below 100 degrees in three weeks! (5) I hope it cools off soon.

(6) I've been busy this summer. (7) Last week cristina and I went to the Central Texas Young Writer's Workshop. (8) It's a

© Macmillan/McGraw-Hill

Name _Emilio Cáceres_ Date _10-26-09_

week-long program that helps young people learn to become authors. (9) I've decided to write a book this summer. (10) I haven't written much yet, but I do have the title picked out.

(11) I'm calling my book *The mystery of Lost Pines*. (12) It's about a boy named Hector and his dog paco. (13) They go hiking in the woods near bastrop and stumble upon an abandoned mine shaft. (14) They find a chest full of old coins, and they try to find out where it came from. (15) I found an old chest in my mom's closet yesterday. (16) I'll send you my book when I'm finished with it. (17) Maybe you can be my editor.

(18) Next week my parents and I are going to spend a week at Uncle John's ranch near Corpus christi. (19) We're going to help pick oranges. (20) We may also help pick grapefruit. (21) I wish you were going to be there!

Your friend,

Maria

which sentence doe not belong

---

1 What change, if any, should be made in sentence 2?

  A Add a comma after *hot*

  B Change *dallas* to **Dallas**

  C Change *summer* to **Summer**

  D Make no change

2 What change, if any, should be made in sentence 3?

  A Change *It's* to **Its**

  B Add a comma after *here*

  C Change *seguin* to **Seguin**

  D Make no change

Name_____ Date_____

3 What change, if any, should be made in sentence 4?

   A Change **don't** to **dont'**

   B Add a comma after **degrees**

   C Change the exclamation mark after **weeks** to a question mark

   (D) Make no change

4 What change, if any, should be made in sentence 7?

   A Change **week** to **Week**

   (B) Change **cristina** to **Cristina**

   C Change **Writer's** to **writer's**

   D Make no change

5 How should the title in sentence 11 be written?

   A *The mystery of lost Pines*

   B *The Mystery Of Lost Pines*

   (C) *The Mystery of Lost Pines*

   D *The Mystery of lost pines*

6 What change, if any, should be made in sentence 12?

   A Change **boy** to **Boy**

   B Change **named** to **namd**

   (C) Change **paco** to **Paco**

   D Make no change

7 What change, if any, should be made in sentence 13?

   A Change **woods** to **Woods**

   (B) Change **bastrop** to **Bastrop**

   C Add **they** before **stumble**

   D Make no change

8 Which sentence does **NOT** belong in the letter?

   A Sentence 14

   (B) Sentence 15

   C Sentence 16

   D Sentence 17

© Macmillan/McGraw-Hill

Name_____ **Date**_____

9 What change, if any, should be made in sentence 18?

    A Change *parents* to **Parents**

    B Change *I* to **me**

    C Change *Corpus christi* to **Corpus Christi**

    D Make no change

10 Which sentence can **BEST** be added after sentence 21?

    A Cristina enjoys writing, too.

    B Many oranges come from Florida.

    C Bananas are my favorite fruit.

    D We always have a great time together.

Name_____ **Date**_____

WRITE

Write a composition about the thing you enjoy doing the most.

The box below will help you write your composition. Then, on another piece of paper write your composition.

REMEMBER TO—

☐ write about the thing you enjoy doing the most

☐ make sure that every sentence helps make your composition clearer

☐ include details and vivid descriptive language to help the reader understand what you enjoy so much about your subject

☐ check your spelling, capitalization, punctuation, and grammar carefully

Check that all proper nouns begin with a capital letter.

© Macmillan/McGraw-Hill

Name *Emilio Cáceres*   Date *10-30-09*

REVIEW

Main Idea and Supporting Details

The **main idea** tells you what a selection is all about. The **supporting details** in the selection help you to understand the main idea.

Read the selection. Then answer the questions that follow.

Amazing Sea Otters

Sea otters are amazing animals. They live in cool ocean waters near the shore. These mammals can grow to five feet in length and weigh up to 85 pounds. A sea otter's thick fur traps air, keeping its skin dry and warm. For many years, they were hunted for their fur. Today, laws protect them from hunters.

Sea otters spend almost all their time in the water. They sleep while floating on their backs. They even eat while floating on their backs! Here is how a sea otter might eat a meal. First, it dives to the ocean floor and finds a flat rock. Then, it looks around for a tasty clam. As the otter floats on its back, it holds the rock on its stomach. It hits the hard shellfish against the rock until it breaks open. Then the otter eats the tender inner part.

Otters stay busy cracking open and eating shellfish. In fact, many otters eat as much as one-fifth of their body weight each day. Just think—if you were an 85-pound otter, you would eat about 17 pounds of clams today, and that's without the shells!

1   What is the main idea of this selection?

Sea otters are amazing Animals.

2   List three details that best support the main idea in this selection.

They sleep while floating on the oceano.

_____

_____

Name Emilio Cáceres   **Date** 10-30-09

#1 Is many about how platypus   60

#3 which detail supports the idea

#2 why people think that Pictures must be a joke.

PRACTICE

Main Idea and Supporting Details

Read the selection. Then read each question that follows the selection. Decide which is the best answer to each question. Mark the letter for that answer.

Australia is home to many unusual birds, reptiles, and mammals—for example, kangaroos and koalas. This article tells about one of the most unusual creatures in the Land Down Under. This creature is so different that at first people in other parts of the world had a hard time believing that it really existed.

The Platypus

1   The duck-billed platypus lives in eastern Australia and Tasmania. It is one of nature's strangest creatures. When people in Europe first saw pictures of the platypus, they thought someone was playing a joke on them.

2   The platypus appears to be a combination of several different animals. One person described it as "half bird, half beast." Another said it looked like a small otter. Others described the animal as a kind of <u>duck</u>. Almost everyone who saw the platypus agreed that it looked as if it were part fish, part bird, and part four-legged mammal.

3   It's easy to understand why people were so confused about the platypus. The animal lives along waterways. Its webbed feet and broad, flat tail make it an excellent swimmer. This explains why some people thought it must be some kind of fish. But the platypus also has a flat hairless <u>bill</u>, which makes it look like a duck. So others thought it was a bird. Finally, the platypus is about the size of a small cat. Its body is covered with a thick coat of fur, and it has four legs. These characteristics reminded people of mammals.

4   Today we know that the platypus is a mammal. Mammals are a group of animals whose females feed their young with milk from

© Macmillan/McGraw-Hill

#1

#4

#8

#9

Name_____ Date_____

their own body. Most mammals also <u>bear</u> their young alive, but the platypus does not do this. A platypus lays eggs, like a bird or a reptile. Only one other animal is a mammal that also lays eggs. This is the echidna (i-KID-nuh), also called the spiny anteater, which lives in Australia and New Guinea.

5   The platypus is a solitary animal. Each animal lives alone, except when the female is nursing her young. The male and the female each dig a separate burrow in a <u>bank</u> along a waterway. The female builds a nest of leaves and grass at the end of her burrow and lays one or two tiny eggs. Once in a while, she may lay three. Each egg is about a half inch in diameter and has a tough, leathery shell. After about ten days, the young platypuses hatch. Although they are able to swim immediately, the young ones will remain in the burrow with their mother for about four months.

6   The platypus has claws on its feet, which it uses to dig up food such as worms, snail, frogs, insects, and small fish. While it is digging, the webbing on its feet folds back to expose the claws. Then, it stores what it has found in a cheek pouch, one located on either side of its mouth, and continues looking for more food. The male has hollow places near his claws. These are connected to a poison gland, which the male uses to defend himself from other males or from humans and their dogs. Australia is full of poisonous snakes, but the male platypus is the only Australian mammal that is poisonous.

7   However, you don't have to worry about being poisoned by a platypus unless you try to harm one. The animals are very shy and spend most of their time in their burrows. Most people see a platypus only when it is swimming. Perhaps you will see one someday. If so, you may realize why people once thought the animal was someone's idea of a joke.

#6 The male and female dig seperate burrows.

Name_____ Date_____

1 This selection is mainly about how the platypus—

A is a native of Australia

B is the only poisonous Australian mammal

C is an unusual animal

D is a cousin of the spiny anteater

2 Why did people think its pictures must be a joke?

A They had never seen an otter before.

B It looked like a combination of many different animals.

C They knew nothing about Australian wildlife.

D They thought only snakes were poisonous.

3 Which detail supports the idea that the platypus is a mammal?

A It lays eggs.

B It is a solitary animal.

C The female nurses its young with milk from its own body.

D It does not bear its young alive.

4 Paragraph 3 is mainly about—

A how the platypus has characteristics of different kinds of animals

B how the platypus has webbed feet and a broad, flat tail

C why many people thought the platypus was a kind of duck

D how the common name for it is "duck-billed platypus"

5 Paragraph 7 is mainly about—

A how the platypus uses its claws to dig up food

B how the platypus is a shy animal

C how the male platypus is poisonous

D why there is a good chance you'll see a platypus when you go swimming

© Macmillan/McGraw-Hill

Name_____ Date_____

6 The male and female platypus dig separate burrows. Which main idea does this detail support?

A   The platypus used to be hunted for its fur.

B   The platypus is a solitary animal.

C   The female usually lays one or two eggs in her burrow.

D   The platypus digs its burrows in the banks of streams and rivers.

7 In paragraph 2, the word <u>duck</u> means—

A   to bend down to avoid being hit

B   a kind of truck that can drive through water

C   a bird that swims

D   a kind of cotton used to make tents and boat sails

P. 2

8 In paragraph 3, the word <u>bill</u> means—

A   a bird's beak

B   a paper stating that one owes money

C   a possible law presented to Congress

D   a piece of paper money, as a dollar bill

P. 3

9 In paragraph 4, the word <u>bear</u> means—

A   a large, woodland mammal

B   to carry

C   to hold up or support

D   to give birth to

P.

10 In paragraph 5, the word <u>bank</u> means—

A   a place of business that deals with money

B   the ground along a river or stream

C   to turn to one side, as a plane

D   a small container for coins

P. 5

Name _Emilio Cáceres_   Date _11/4/09_

REVIEW

Subject-Verb Agreement

The subject and verb in a sentence must agree. They must both be singular or plural. **Follow these rules for subject-verb agreement:**

* Add -*s* to most present-tense verbs if the subject is singular.

  The **Potomac River flows** southeast across the Piedmont.

* Add -*es* to present-tense verbs that end in *s, ch, sh, x,* or *z.*

  My **uncle teaches** second grade at Roanoke Elementary School.

* Do not add -*s* or -*es* to verbs if the subject is plural or if it is *I* or *you.*

  Doctors agree that exercise is necessary for good health.

  You live near my cousins, Amy and Jennifer.

Also be sure that verbs agree in **tense**. For example, do not switch back and forth between present-tense and past-tense verbs.

> *Incorrect:* Joe and I **were talking**. He **says** he **likes** my **shoes**.
> *Correct:* Joe and I **were talking**. He **said** he **liked** my **shoes**.

Underline the verb that agrees with the subject.

1. Jacob (use, uses) a computer to do his homework.

2. Bald eagles (make, makes) their homes near Lake Buchanan.

3. I (want, wants) to learn more about how to fix bicycles.

4. Porsha's grandmother (eat, eats) dinner with her each Sunday.

5. Many Texans (enjoy, enjoys) hiking and boating.

© Macmillan/McGraw-Hill

Name Emilio Cáceres   **Date** 11/05/09

 # PRACTICE

Subject-Verb Agreement

Ella is a fourth grader at Barbara Jordan Elementary School. She is writing a story about her friend Pete and his brother John. Read her story and decide which corrections she might make. Then answer the questions that follow.

One Quiet Afternoon

(1) John sat alone in the bedroom. (2) The room was dark because the shades was pulled down. (3) This was the third day that John had been sitting in the dark. (4) He had the measles. (5) He had listened to the radio until his ears buzzed. (6) He even do the homework that his brother Pete had brought home for him. (7) John was good at reading, and Pete was good at math. (8) Now he did what he always did when he waited for his brother to come home from school. (9) He looked at the closed-up windows and tried to picture what was going on right outside his room.

(10) First came the sound of the spaceship. (11) He imagine he could hear the little aliens talking in their strange language. (12) They were only six inches tall, so the backyard was like a jungle. (13) John laughed as he imagined the aliens bumping into his football on the lawn and trying to talk with it. (14) When the ball didn't talk back, the little aliens tried to decide what it was. (15) Football is a good game to play, but John didn't get to play much because you needed so many people to

© Macmillan/McGraw-Hill

Name_____ **Date**_____

make up two teams. (16) One brave little alien went up to the ball and bit it, thinking it might be something good to eat. (17) She jumped back as a hiss of air leaked out of the ball from the hole she had made.

(18) The leader of the group got them together and led them closer to the house. (19) Suddenly the ground began to shake as King, John's dog, ran toward them. (20) All the little aliens made a circle around the dog and gave King a low bow. (21) King barked so loud that they all fell down. (22) King thought the aliens was Pete's toy soldiers, and he must not play with them. (23) King lay down and watched as the little aliens got up and dusted themselves off. (24) They were so shaken that they got back on board their spaceship and blasted off.

(25) Pete came running into the dark room. (26) "You won't believe what you missed at school today," Pete exclaimed excitedly.

(27) "Well, you won't believe what you missed here," replied John with a smile.

Name_____ Date_____

1 What change, if any, should be made in sentence 2?

  A Change *was dark* to **were dark**

  B Change *was pulled* to **were pulled**

  C Change *because* to **so**

  D Make no change

2 What is the main idea of the first paragraph?

  A John's bedroom is dark.

  B John is good at reading.

  C John is bored.

  D John feels sick.

3 What change, if any, should be made in sentence 6?

  A Change *He* to **Pete**

  B Change *even do* to **had even done**

  C Change *brought* to **bring**

  D Make no change

4 What sentence does **NOT** belong in the first paragraph?

  A Sentence 4

  B Sentence 5

  C Sentence 7

  D Sentence 9

5 What change, if any, should be made in sentence 11?

  A Change *could hear* to **could heard**

  B Change *imagine* to **imagined**

  C Change *talking* to **talkking**

  D Make no change

6 What is the main idea of the second paragraph?

  A Aliens eat footballs.

  B Aliens discover a jungle.

  C John imagines aliens have landed outside.

  D Aliens are six inches tall.

© Macmillan/McGraw-Hill

Name_____ **Date**_____

7 What sentence does **NOT** belong in paragraph 2?

   A Sentence 13

   B Sentence 14

   C Sentence 15

   D Sentence 16

8 What change, if any, should be made in sentence 19?

   A Change *began* to **begins**

   B Take out the comma after *John's dog*

   C Change *ran* to **runs**

   D Make no change

9 What change, if any, should be made in sentence 22?

   A Change *thought* to **thinks**

   B Change *aliens* to **ailens**

   C Change *was* to **were**

   D Make no change

10 Ella may decide to revise her story so that it is all a fantasy. She would need to change—

   A the beginning and the middle

   B the middle

   C the end

   D the beginning and the end

Name_____ **Date**_____

WRITE

Write a composition describing a perfect day at school.

The box below will help you write your composition. Then, on another piece of paper write your composition.

REMEMBER TO—

📖 write about a perfect day at school

📖 make sure that every sentence is clear and necessary and that there is a logical flow of ideas from beginning to end

📖 include descriptions and details to help the reader understand what you are saying

📖 check your spelling, capitalization, punctuation, and grammar carefully

Make sure your subjects and verbs agree.

Name _Emilio Cáceres_   Date _1꣠/05/09_

REVIEW

Draw Inferences

Sometimes readers must **make inferences**, or draw conclusions about what the author suggests but does not state. To make an inference, use the clues provided by the author and your own experiences. Your inferences should be consistent with the story.

Read the selection. Then answer the questions that follow.

Midnight at Canyon Camp

It was too hot to sleep. Tanya kicked the covers off of the bed. Her mom had promised Tanya that she would love Canyon Camp. The camp brochure promised fun and excitement. Tanya could not imagine finding excitement at this place.

Tanya dozed off to sleep. Suddenly, she was awakened by a crashing noise, followed by a low growling sound. Sue, Tanya's roommate, jumped up.

"What in the world was that?" Sue asked, frightened.

"I don't know," Tanya replied, trying to sound brave.

Just then, the growling noises began again. Tanya and Sue crouched together in the corner. "If we ever get out of this, I'll never complain about a lack of excitement again," promised Tanya.

1 What do you think is making the noise outside the cabin? What clues did you use to make this inference?

  A Bear, Because in the picture is a bear.

2 Think about what Tanya said and did in the passage. What do you think she might do the next morning?

  She tought that she was scared. She may
  said the story to his friends make
  scary.

Name *Emilio Cáceres*   Date *11/05/09*

*#1 What is the Setting. #2 Kind of Storm #3Details
about the Storm #4 why cory is worried about*

TAKS PRACTICE *his mother. #6 why Cory's
father thinks, #7 Cory's act with horses
#8 how come back home #9 mostly about*

Draw Inferences *#q what will be hapen, Cory*

**Read the selection. Then read each question that follows the
selection. Decide which is the best answer to each question.
Mark the letter for that answer.**

*some persons wainting
for a strong
storm.*

Waiting Out the Storm

1   Zipping up his winter jacket, Cory ran to the barn. "The radio
says a big storm is on the way," he called to his father. "I'll go start
rounding up the horses."

2   "I was going to let the cows out into the pasture," said his father.
"But if the storm is really bad, they could get lost."

3   Cory jumped on his bike and rode toward the far pasture. Some
of the horses saw him coming and galloped to the fence. Cory often
gave them apples and pieces of sugar, so they welcomed him. But
today he was in too much of a hurry. He opened the gate that led
them back to the barn.

4   "Are Mom and Janet on their way back to the ranch?" Cory
asked. His voice was full of worry. "Couldn't they be trapped on
their way up the hill? Should we take the truck and get them? We
don't want them to be stuck on the hillside the way we were." Cory
was so worried he couldn't stop chattering.

5   "Don't be scared, Son," said his father in a soft voice. "We have a
lot more warning for this storm than we did for that one. Your mom
and sister will be fine. And your mother, in case you didn't know, is
a terrific driver in any kind of weather." However, when he turned
away, he looked tense and serious.

6   As the temperatures continued to drop, Cory and his father
piled plenty of feed hay in the stalls for the animals. Then they
filled the water troughs. The Loomis house was a quarter mile away
from the barn. "We may not be able to get back here once the storm
starts," said Mr. Loomis. "We have to be sure the horses and cows
have food and water for a while."

Name_____ Date_____

7   Suddenly Mr. Loomis's cell phone rang. Cory's eyes lit up. "I'll bet that's Mom and Sis," he said. His dad answered and talked for a few moments. Then he handed the phone to Cory. "Hey, little brother," sang out his sister's voice. "You'd better be sure you feed Harry, or I'll be sure to glue your bedroom door shut." Cory grinned and passed the phone to his father. Mr. Loomis talked some more and then hung up. Concern wrinkled his forehead.

8   "The people in town told Mom she shouldn't try to get home now. The storm is coming on too fast. Mom thinks she and Janet should wait until later when the roads are cleared. I guess I agree with that. Well, we'd better get to the house and get ready."

9   "Well, I guess I agree, too," said Cory. "They'll be safer in town than on the road. But I still wish they were here."

10   The two returned to the house, with Cory riding ahead of his dad. They brought in logs for the fireplace and built a roaring fire. "We can pretend we live out on the frontier a hundred years ago," joked Cory's father, trying to wipe the worry off his son's face. Then he had an idea. He disappeared into the kitchen and returned with a bag of marshmallows. "Find a good stick for roasting these," he said to Cory.

11   Father and son roasted marshmallows in the fireplace and listened to the rising wind that shook the windows. As they watched the storm surround the house, the phone suddenly rang again. Cory's dad listened, and then his face broke into a smile as he hung up. "Your mom and Janet are going to ride with the first plow that comes up the hill," he said. The two settled down to await the storm. "I'm glad we had time to plan for this one," sighed Cory.

Leo

Name Emilio Cáceres   **Date** 11/05/09

1 What is the setting of this story?

A A house on the prairie

B A house in the tropics

C A ranch up in the hills

D A ranch in the desert

2 What kind of storm is expected?

A A dust storm

B A blizzard

C A tornado

D A thunderstorm

3 Which details helped you decide what kind of storm it was?

A The need to get the horses and cows into the barn

B The winter jacket, falling temperatures, and fear of getting trapped

C The piling up of hay for the horses and roasting of marshmallows

D The two cell phone calls

4 Why is Cory so worried about his mother and sister?

A Cory is not very courageous.

B Cory thinks his mother is not a good driver.

C Cory was stuck in a storm before.

D Cory doesn't know that his parents have cell phones.

5 In paragraph 7, what does the word passed mean?

A Threw a football

B Walked or drove by

C Spent time

D Handed from one person to another

P. 7

Name_____ Date_____

6 Why does Cory's father probably think they might not be able to reach the barn for a while?

A He thinks winds will blow the barn away.

B Snowdrifts might block their path to the barn.

C The Loomises are all going out of town.

D Heavy rains may wash out the path to the barn.

7 The way Cory acts with the horses suggests that he is—

A kind

B fun-loving

C careless

D forgetful

8 How will Mrs. Loomis and Janet return home?

A In a truck

B In a snowplow

C In their car

D On horseback

9 This story is mostly about—

A a family planning for a snowstorm

B the different ways to use cell phones

C the relationship between a boy and the horses on his ranch

D the relationship between a brother and sister

10 What will most likely happen to Cory in the future?

A He will become less courageous.

B He will realize that danger is easier to face with good planning.

C He will get his bedroom door glued shut by Janet.

D He will look forward to the next big storm.

© Macmillan/McGraw-Hill

Name_____ Date_____

REVIEW

Editing for Grammar and Usage

When you proofread your writing, make sure that you have written complete sentences and that your sentences do not all sound the same. Watch for run-on sentences and correct any you find. Also check to make sure you have used nouns, pronouns, verbs, adjectives, and adverbs correctly.

Read the sentences. Rewrite them correctly on the lines below. If no corrections are necessary, write *Make no change*.

1   The crowd shouted loud as the runner scored.

    _Make no change_____

2   Frank throwed the ball as hard as he could to Simon.

    Frank throw the ball as he could to Simon.

3   Joan and my sister is going to practice with us today.

    Joan and my sistere are going to practice with us today,

4   Tawanna is the faster runner on the team.

    _Make no change_____

5   Jodie hit the ball, and she ran quickly to first base.

    Jodie hit the ball and she ran quickly to first base

Take your time editing and proofreading your work. Make sure your sentences are clear and complete.

Name *Emilia Cáceres* **Date**

PRACTICE

Editing for Grammar and Usage

Marta is a fourth grader at Liberty Elementary School. She is writing a paper about her first science fair. Read her draft, considering which improvements and corrections she might make. Then answer the questions that follow.

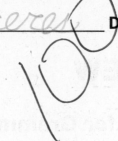

My First Science Fair

#1   (1) I sat looking glum out the kitchen window. (2) My teacher had

asked I to enter the science fair. (3) But I had no idea what to do.

(4) "What's wrong, Marta?" my mother asked. (5) I told she about the

#3

science fair.

#4 → (6) "I don't knows where to start," I said with a frown.

(7) "Well," my mother said. (8) "You love plants. (9) How about

studying plants?"

(10) "I wonder what experiment I could do with plants?" I thought.

#6

(11) I went to bed thinking about plants. (12) I

also thought about what to wear in the morning. (13)

←#5

When I awoke, I had an idea. (14) I could study the effects

off sunlight on plant growth. (15) My teacher suggested

that I compare the effects of sunlight and lamplight on

plants. (16) I liked that idea.

↓

#7

© Macmillan/McGraw-Hill

Name _Emilia Cáceres_ **Date** _____

#8 (17) First, I bought two ivy plants. (18) I measured the height of each plant. (19) Next, I put one ivy in a sunny window. (20) I put the other under a lamp. (21) Every three days, I measured the plants again. (22) I wrote the results in a notebook. #9

(23) On the day of the fair, I set up my experiment in the school #10 library. (24) The plant that had grown in the sunlight was much tallest than the one that had grown under the lamp. (25) I felt proud of what I had done. (26) Maybe I'll be a scientist one day.

---

1 What change, if any, should be made in sentence 1?

   A Change *sat* to *sits*

   B Change *glum* to *glumly*

   C Change *kitchen* to *kichen*

   D Make no change

S.1

2 What change, if any, should be made in sentence 2?

   A Change *asked* to *ask*

   B Change *I* to *me*

S.2   **C** Change *enter* to *entering*

   D Make no change

3 What change, if any, should be made in sentence 5?

   A Change *told* to *tell*

   B Change *she* to *her*

   C Change the period after *fair* to a question mark

   D Make no change

S.5

4 What change, if any, should be made in sentence 6?

   A Change *don't* to *dont'*

   B Change *knows* to *know*

   C Change *said* to *says*

   D Make no change

S.6

Name _Emilia_____ Date _____

5 What change, if any, should be made in sentence 14?

   A Change *studies* to **study**

   B Change *off* to **of**

   C Add a comma after *sunlight*

   D Make no change

S.14

6 Which sentence does **NOT** belong in the sixth paragraph?

   A Sentence 11

   B Sentence 12

   C Sentence 15

   D Sentence 16

P.6

7 Which sentence could **BEST** be added after sentence 16?

   A My parents both enjoy gardening.

   B That was the experiment I would do.

   C My teacher loves science projects.

   D Electricity is a fascinating subject.

S.16

8 What change, if any, should be made in sentence 19?

   A Change *put* to **puts**

   B Change *put* to **have put**

   C Change *sunny* to **suny**

   D Make no change

S.19

Name _Emilio_   Date _____

9   What is the **BEST** way to combine sentences 21 and 22?

   A   Every three days, I measured the plants again and notebook.

   B   Every three days, I wrote the results in a notebook.

   C   Every three days, I measured the plants again and wrote the results in a notebook.

   D   Every three days, I measured the plants again, but I wrote the results in a notebook.

10 What change, if any, should be made in sentence 24?

   A   Change *grown* to **growed**

   B   Change *was* to **were**

   C   Change *tallest* to **taller**

   D   Make no change

S.24

Name_____ **Date**_____

WRITE

Write a composition about something your school should celebrate.

The box below will help you write your composition. Then, write your composition on another piece of paper.

REMEMBER TO—

- ☐ write about something your school should celebrate

- ☐ make sure that every sentence helps make your composition clearer

- ☐ include details to help the reader picture what you are saying

- ☐ check your spelling, capitalization, punctuation, and grammar in the sentences .... *Check your writing to make sure your grammar is correct.*

Name_____ Date_____

REVIEW

Summarize

A **summary** is a short retelling in your own words. To summarize a story, describe the setting, the main characters, and the most important events. To summarize other kinds of writing, state the main idea and the most important points.

Read the selection. Then answer the questions that follow.

Tim the Robin

Tim the robin was afraid to fly. His brother Jack and sister Greta could swoop and loop, but not poor Tim. He just clung desperately to the big oak tree's branches and watched his brother and sister fly by. As they whizzed past him, they'd taunt, "Tim, Tim, why don't you just walk?"

Tim's only friend was a squirrel named Amy, who loved to scurry up the trunk of the oak tree. One day, Tim heard Amy squealing from a branch above. Amy was falling. Without thinking, Tim swooped down and caught Amy by the nape of the neck, just as she was about to hit the ground. As they softly landed, Amy cheered, "Tim, you saved me! And you can fly!"

1 What is the setting?

I think they're in the forest

2 Who are the characters?

Tim, Greta, Amy, Jack

3 What happens?

Amy was falling without thinking

It's a good idea to stop and summarize every few paragraphs as you read. Write labels next to paragraphs.

Name_____ Date_____

PRACTICE

Summarize

Read the selection. Then read each question that follows the
selection. Decide which is the best answer to each question.
Mark the letter for that answer.

Gumming Things Up

1   Have you ever reached under a desk top or seat
bottom only to find an ugly, messy piece of old chewing
gum? Have you ever been annoyed by talking with
someone who is blowing bubbles in your face or loudly
chewing and snapping their gum? Have you ever
walked through a parking lot on a warm day only to
step onto a nasty wad of melting gum? The next time
some selfish, careless gum chewer causes you to suffer
in one of those ways, you could yell, "Remember the
Alamo!"

2   That's right! You can vent your frustration on the Mexican
general who led the charge against the Texans at the Alamo. In the
1830s, when Texans were fighting for their independence from
Mexico, General Santa Anna led an army of 5,000 into San Antonio.
Two hundred people were killed by Santa Anna's army at the
Alamo, a fort there. After the attack, Texans took up the battle cry
"Remember the Alamo!" Under the command of General Sam
Houston, they defeated Santa Anna's army and forced Mexico to
give Texas its independence. Several years later, Santa Anna was
forced to leave Mexico and moved to Staten Island, New York.

3   The defeated general brought with him one of his homeland's
treats—large chunks of the milky sap from a jungle tree, the
sapodilla. Known to the Aztec people as *chictli*, the tasteless gum
was introduced by Santa Anna to Thomas Adams, an inventor and
neighbor on Staten Island. Adams imported large amounts of the
gum, or chicle, from Mexico hoping to create a cheap form of rubber.
Though he failed, he noticed that his son, like Santa Anna, loved to

Name_____ Date_____

chew chicle. Adams began selling chicle as a replacement for the wax balls that many people chewed at the time.

4   Thomas Adams's first small, tasteless chicle balls went on sale in February 1871. Gum proved to be more popular than wax, and soon it was sold in long, thin strips that could be torn off into one-penny lengths.

5   The first person to flavor gum was John Colgan from Louisville, Kentucky, in 1875. He was not thinking of making candy when he mixed chicle gum with balsam of tolu, then a standard cough syrup. Colgan was trying to invent a fun way for children to take their cough medicine.

6   When word got back to Adams, he began to make flavored gum balls and selling them in train stations. One of his popular flavors was "Black Jack," a licorice-tasting gum.

7   In 1910, William Wrigley, Jr., creator of the best-selling spearmint flavor, thought of a way to get even more people chewing gum. He sent four free sticks to each of the 1.5 million people listed in the telephone directory. He became America's top gum maker.

8   During World War I and World War II, the United States Armed Forces included gum in soldiers' food rations. Soldiers chewed five times as much gum as the average person. Soldiers stationed in Alaska gave the gum to the Inuit, who soon replaced their centuries-old tradition of chewing whale blubber with gum.

9   So, from its Alamo-related beginnings all the way to Alaska, chewing gum found a sticky place in America's history. After over a hundred years of gum chewing, I hope someone's next invention will be an easy way to get messy gum off the bottom of our shoes.

1   This selection is—

   A   nonfiction

   B   fiction

   C   a story

   D   a journal entry

2   The reader can tell from paragraph 1 that the writer—

   A   does not like gum chewers

   B   enjoys licorice gum

   C   thinks gum should be free

   D   enjoys chewing wax

© Macmillan/McGraw-Hill

Name_____ Date_____

3 In paragraph 2, the word vent means—

   A tear apart

   B an opening in a heating pipe

   C a fold in the side of a shirt

   D release

4 Paragraph 3 is mostly about—

   A why Santa Anna chewed chicle

   B how chicle replaced wax balls

   C why Adams wanted to create a cheap form of rubber

   D how General Santa Anna introduced chicle to an inventor on Staten Island

5 In paragraph 3, the word imported means—

   A something important

   B a place for ships to dock

   C brought from another country

   D done with great care

6 If John Colgan's invention had been a complete success, when would we buy gum today?

   A When we are on vacation in Mexico

   B When we have a cold

   C When we visit the Alamo

   D When we felt like eating licorice

7 The chart below follows the path that gum traveled in the passage.

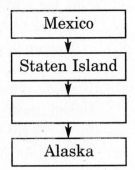

| Mexico |
| Staten Island |
| |
| Alaska |

Which place belongs in the empty box?

   A San Antonio

   B Kentucky

   C Chicago

   D Adams

Name_____ Date_____

8 Which is the best summary of this article?

   A Chewing gum is bad because people who chew it are careless and selfish. It gets stuck on everything especially the bottom of your shoes.

   B Gum was shipped in from Mexico to Staten Island. It was sold in Kentucky, New York, Alaska, and all over the United States to addresses found in telephone directories.

   C Gum was introduced to the United States by Santa Anna, a Mexican general. At first, gum was flavorless, but later flavors were added. Gum became more and more popular.

   D Gum was originally tasteless and unpopular. It replaced chewing wax when people began to add flavors to it. Spearmint is one popular flavor.

9 Which of these best describes the writer's overall tone in this selection?

   A Serious

   B Light-hearted

   C Dramatic

   D Dark and frightening

10 The most likely reason the author wrote this article was to—

   A convince people to stop chewing gum

   B explain how gum came to the United States

   C explain how gum became flavored

   D convince the reader that chewing gum is good for a cough

© Macmillan/McGraw-Hill

Name_____ Date_____

REVIEW

Checking for Spelling

When you proofread your writing, be sure to check for mistakes in spelling. If you are unsure of the correct spelling of a word, you can look it up in a dictionary.

Read the paragraph. Then answer the questions below.

A Report on Comets

Samantha and Luiz worked together on their class science project. They decided to <u>reserch</u> comets. They had worked very hard and wrote a <u>wonderfull</u> report. In addition to their paper, Luiz thought that they should make a poster of a comet. Samantha, however, believed it would be more exciting to build a <u>modal</u> of a comet, brightly painted in red and yellow. They decided to walk to the craft store to buy <u>materials</u>.

1 In the second sentence, <u>reserch</u> should be written—

   research

2 In the third sentence, <u>wonderfull</u> should be written—

   wonderful

3 In the fifth sentence, <u>modal</u> should be written—

   model

4 In the sixth sentence, <u>matterials</u> should be written—

   materials

If you are unsure how to spell a word and cannot use a dictionary, try writing the word out several ways.

© Macmillan/McGraw-Hill

Name_____ Date_____

PRACTICE

Checking for Spelling

Tai is a fourth grader at Columbus Elementary School. He is writing a report about tornadoes. Read his report and think about improvements he might make. Then answer the questions that follow.

Tornadoes

(1) A tornado is a rapidly spinning columm of wind that forms under a thundercloud. (2) Tornadoes, also called *twisters*, are the most violent of all stormes. (3) A tornado can contain winds of over 300 miles per hour. (4) It can lift cars into the air. (5) It can lift mobile homes into the air. (6) A tornado can distroy nearly everything in its path.

(7) Tornadoes can happen at any time in the year. (8) Most tornadoes occur in late spring and early summer. (9) They usualy occur between the hours of 4:00 p.m. and 8:00 p.m.

(10) More tornadoes occur in the United States than in any other place in the world, with Australia ranking second. (11) Texas has reccorded more tornadoes than any other state, making Texas the Tornado Capital of the World.

Name_____ **Date**_____

(12) The greatest number of tornadoes in a single year occurred in 1967, when 232 tornadoes hit the ground. (13) The second highest number occurred in 1995, when 223 tornadoes struck Texas. (14) The largest number of tornadoes in one month occurred in September of 1967, when 124 tornadoes struck as a ressult of winds and rain caused by Hurricane Beulah. (15) Hurricanes can also be very destructive. (16) A single-day record was set on September 20, 1967, when 67 tornadoes hit.

1 What change, if any, should be made in sentence 1?

   A Change *rapidly* to *rapid*

   B Change *columm* to *column*

   C Change *thundercloud* to *thunderclowd*

   D Make no change

2 What change, if any, should be made in sentence 2?

   A Change *also* to *allso*

   B Take out the comma after *twisters*

   C Change *stormes* to *storms*

   D Make no change

Name_____ Date_____

3 What change, if any, should be made in sentence 3?

  A Change *contain* to **contane**

  B Add a comma after *winds*

  C Change *per hour* to **Per Hour**

  D Make no change

4 What is the **BEST** way to combine sentences 4 and 5?

  A It can lift cars and mobile homes into the air.

  B It can lift cars into the air, it can lift mobile homes into the air.

  C It can lift cars into the air, but it can lift mobile homes into the air.

  D It can lift cars, and mobile homes, into the air.

5 What change, if any, should be made in sentence 6?

  A Change *distroy* to **destroy**

  B Change *nearly* to **near**

  C Change *its* to **it's**

  D Make no change

6 What is the **BEST** way to combine sentences 7 and 8?

  A Tornadoes can happen at any time in the year, most tornadoes occur in late spring and early summer.

  B Tornadoes can happen at any time in the year, with most tornadoes occur in late spring and early summer.

  C Tornadoes can happen at any time in the year, but most tornadoes occur in late spring and early summer.

  D Tornadoes can happen at any time, most tornadoes occur in late spring and early summer.

Name_____ Date_____

7 What change, if any, should be made in sentence 9?

A   Change *They* to **Their**

B   Change *usualy* to **usually**

C   Change *between* to **be tween**

D   Make no change

8 What change, if any, should be made in sentence 11?

A   Change *has* to **have**

B   Change *reccorded* to **recorded**

C   Add a comma between *Texas* and *the*

D   Make no change

9 What change, if any, should be made in sentence 14?

A   Change *largest* to **larger**

B   Add a comma after *struck*

C   Change *ressult* to **result**

D   Make no change

10 Which sentence does **NOT** belong in the last paragraph?

A   Sentence 13

B   Sentence 14

C   Sentence 15

D   Sentence 16

© Macmillan/McGraw-Hill

Name_____ Date_____

WRITE

Write a composition about your favorite place.

The box below will help you write your composition. Then write your composition on another piece of paper.

REMEMBER TO—

❑ write about your favorite place

❑ make sure that every sentence helps make your descriptions clear

❑ include details to help the reader understand what you are saying

❑ check your spelling, capitalization, punctuation, and grammar

If you are unsure of a word's spelling, try writing it out several different ways.

Name___Emilio_____ Date_1-11-10_____

REVIEW

Prefixes and Suffixes

A **prefix** is added to the beginning of a word. A **suffix** is added to the end of a word. When added to words, these word parts create new words with their own meanings. You can use prefixes and suffixes to help you figure out the meaning of a word.

Look at the table. Then answer the questions that follow.

Prefix	Suffix	Meaning	Example
un-		not, opposite of	unlucky
dis-		not, opposite of	disobey
pre-		before, in front of	prewash
	-less	without	colorless (without color)
	-ful	full of, having lots of	colorful (having lots of color)

1 What prefix can be added to the word <u>happy</u> to describe someone who is sad? Write the new word.

  unhappy

2 What suffix can be added to the word <u>joy</u> to describe someone who is very happy? Write the new word.

  joyful

3 What prefix can be added to the word <u>approve</u> to make a word that means "not approve"? Write the new word.

  disapprove

TEST-TAKING TIP Consider the meaning of the base word when trying to determine the meaning of the whole word. It should make sense in the sentence.

Name __Emilio__   Date __1-11-10__

TAKS PRACTICE

Prefixes and Suffixes

Read the selection. Then read each question that follows the selection. Decide which is the best answer to each question. Mark the letter for that answer.

The Birthday Surprise

1   Kai jumped out of bed before the alarm rang. It was her birthday, and she was anxious to see what the day held in store for her. Her mother had promised that they would do something special today. Kai couldn't wait to find out what the surprise was.

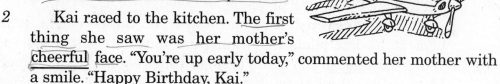

2   Kai raced to the kitchen. The first thing she saw was her mother's cheerful face. "You're up early today," commented her mother with a smile. "Happy Birthday, Kai."

3   On the table next to Kai's plate was a small present. "Can I open it?" she asked excitedly.

4   "I don't see why not," her mother replied.

5   Kai quickly unwrapped her present. Inside the box she found a toy airplane. "What's this, Mom?" Kai asked, looking puzzled.

6   "Well, I know how much you like airplanes, Kai. So, how would you like to take a ride in one today?"

7   "Really? You're the greatest!" Kai gave her mom a playful hug.

8   Kai's mom drove them to the small airport in town. There, waiting for them, was a friendly pilot standing next to a small airplane. "We're going to have a great flight, Kai," said the pilot. "But first I need you to help me with my preflight check."

9   The pilot explained to Kai how important it is to make a careful inspection of the plane before each flight. Kai and the pilot went

Name_____ Date_____

through his checklist thoroughly, and finally the pilot said they were ready for takeoff.

10   Kai climbed into the cockpit and took her seat next to the pilot, making sure not to bump against the many dials, buttons, and switches on the control panel in front of her. The pilot started the engine and disengaged the brake, and the plane moved slowly onto the runway. Kai held her breath as the plane accelerated, rolling faster and faster until the wheels finally left the ground and they were airborne.

11   "Wow," Kai exclaimed, and the pilot smiled.

12   "I've never gotten over the thrill of takeoff," he said, "even after 15 years of flying."

13   Kai didn't think the pilot looked old enough to have been flying planes for 15 years. "How old were you when you started flying?" she asked.

14   "Well," answered the pilot, "I was 17 when I started taking flying lessons. I took my first solo flight when I was 19 and got my pilot's license when I was 20."

15   "I'd love to learn how to fly," Kai said. She watched as the pilot banked the plane to the left. "Do you have to be 20 to get a license?"

16   "No," he answered. "In some states, you can become a licensed pilot at 16. But pilots that young are unusual. Most people that young can't get in the hours of flight time required to be licensed." He paused to check their altitude. "There are plenty of young people who start taking flying lessons at 16, though."

17   Kai once again turned her attention to the view outside. As the plane headed up through the clouds, Kai looked down and watched the ground disappear.

18   "This is unbelievable!" Kai said with a smile. "It's like a whole other world!" As they flew over the clouds, she decided that this was the best birthday she'd ever had.

90

Name_____ **Date**_____

1 In paragraph 2, the word cheerful means—

A gloomy

B full of cheer or gladness

C without cheer or gladness

D unfamiliar

2 In paragraph 5, the word unwrapped means—

A the opposite of *wrapped*

B not pretty

C wrapped tightly

D not pleased

3 In paragraph 7, the word playful means—

A the opposite of *fun*

B without joy

C angry

D full of fun

4 In paragraph 8, the word preflight means—

A after takeoff

B before landing

C before takeoff

D during flight

5 In paragraph 9, the word careful means—

A full of care

B without care

C without interest

D boring

6 Both the pilot and Kai—

A collect toy airplanes

B are young and have never flown before

C enjoy the plane's takeoff

D take turns flying the plane

Name_____ **Date**_____

7 In paragraph 18, the word unbelievable means—

   A almost finished

   B easy to believe

   C hard to believe

   D scary

8 This story is mostly about—

   A a daughter's special birthday gift to her mother

   B a dangerous airplane flight

   C a mother's special birthday gift to her daughter

   D how to check out an airplane before a flight

9 Why did the author include Kai's conversation with the pilot?

   A To show how interested Kai is in flying and how much she wants to be a pilot

   B To give the reader some sense of how friendly and outgoing Kai is

   C To provide background information on another character in the story

   D To create suspense and excitement in the story

10 Which of the following is the best summary of the story?

   A Kai meets an experienced pilot. He tells her about his experiences. She enjoys her chance to learn how to inspect an airplane.

   B Kai can't wait to get the day started. She finds a special present next to her plate at breakfast—a tiny airplane.

   C Kai goes above the clouds in an airplane. She watches the ground disappear beneath her.

   D Kai has a real love of airplanes. Her mother gives her the best birthday gift ever—an airplane flight. Kai has a wonderful time on the flight.

Name Emilia   **Date** 7-10-10

REVIEW

Pronouns

In speaking or writing, a **pronoun** may be used in place of a person, place, or thing. Pronouns replace nouns in sentences.

- A **subject pronoun** is used as the subject of a sentence.

  Example: <u>Sara and Eli</u> love soccer.   <u>They</u> love soccer.

- An **object** pronoun is used as the direct or indirect object after action verbs and as the object of a preposition, such as *to*, *in*, and *for*.

  Example: Mario called <u>his mother</u>.   Mario called <u>her</u>.

Subject Pronouns	Object Pronouns
Singular: I, you, he, she, it **Plural:** we, you, they	**Singular:** me, you, him, her, it **Plural:** us, you, them

On the lines below, write the pronoun that would BEST replace the underlined word or words in each sentence.

1   <u>Paula and Chandra</u> race to school.

    They race to school.

2   Please ask <u>José</u> to come to the office.

    Please ask him to come to the office.

3   Would you give this letter to <u>Michelle</u>?

    Her

4   <u>Daniel</u> is building a tree house.

    he

Name Emilio Caceres   Date 2-10-10

PRACTICE

90

Pronouns

Eric is a fourth grader at Jonesville Elementary School. He is writing a story about a birthday gift. Read his story and look for improvements and corrections he might make. Then answer the questions that follow.

Kevin's Present

(1) Kevin was invited to Lerone's birthday party. (2) She had handed out invitations to his friends and he after school. (3) Kevin wanted to give she something special, but he didn't have money for a present. (4) "Maybe I just won't go to the party," he thought.

(5) Kevin's mother noticed that her son looked very sad that night. (6) "Kev, what's wrong?" she asked. (7) "I haven't never seen you look so down."

(8) Kevin told his mother about the party. (9) She said, "Maybe you don't have money to by Lerone a present. (10) But that doesn't really mean that you can't give her a gift. (11) Why don't you make her something?"

(12) Kevin went upstairs. (13) He sat at his desk. (14) "Well," he thought, "I know how to draw. (15) Why don't I draw a picture of Lerone? (16) I could give her the drawing as a present."

(17) Two hours later, Kevin showed the picture to his mother. (18) "What do you think, Mom?" he asked.

© Macmillan/McGraw-Hill

Name_____ Date_____

(19) Kevin's mother looked carefully. (20) She was amazed at how good it was. (21) "That's one of the finest drawings I've ever seen," she said. (22) "Between you and I, that drawing is better than any present from a store." (23) An artist named Rembrandt did a lot of great drawings.

(24) Kevin was the last to arrive at the party. (25) He walked directly over to Lerone and handed her the gift. (26) She opened it quickly, and she gasped with disbelief. (27) "Kevin," she exclaimed, "no one has ever drawn a picture of I. (28) This is truly beautiful. (29) Thank you!"

1 What change, if any, should be made in sentence 2?

A   Change **had** to **have**

B   Change **his** to **Kevins'**

C   Change **he** to **him**

D   Make no change

S.2

2 What change, if any, should be made in sentence 3?

A   Change **wanted** to **want**

B   Change **she** to **her**

C   Delete the comma before **but**

D   Make no change

S.3

Name_____ Date_____

3 What change, if any, should be made in sentence 7?

  A Change *I haven't* to *I've*

  B Change *seen* to *seed*

  C Change *look* to *looks*

  D Make no change

4 What change, if any, should be made in sentence 9?

  A Change *said* to *sed*

  B Change *by* to *buy*

  C Change the period after *present* to a question mark

  D Make no change

5 Which is the **BEST** way to combine sentences 12 and 13?

  A Kevin went upstairs, he sat at his desk.

  B Kevin went upstairs, sitting at his desk.

  C Kevin went upstairs and sat at his desk.

  D Kevin, went upstairs, and then he sat at his desk.

6 What change, if any, should be made in sentence 19?

  A Change *Kevin's* to *Her*

  B Change *looked* to *lookd*

  C Change *carefully* to *carefuly*

  D Make no change

7 The meaning of sentence 20 can be improved by changing *it* to—

  A Kevin

  B the picture

  C the party

  D Kevin's talent

8 What change, if any, should be made in sentence 22?

  A Change *I* to *me*

  B Change *better* to *best*

  C Change the period after *store* to a comma

  D Make no change

© Macmillan/McGraw-Hill

TAKS Writing Practice Exercises • Grade 4

Name_____ **Date**_____

9 Which sentence does **NOT** belong in this paper?

(A) Sentence 23

B Sentence 25

C Sentence 26

D Sentence 27

S.23

10 What change, if any, should be made in sentence 27?

A Change the comma after *Kevin* to a period

B Change *has* to **have**

(C) Change *I* to **me**

D Make no change

S27

Name_____ **Date**_____

WRITE

Write about a famous person you would like to meet.

The box below will help you write your composition. Then, write your composition on another piece of paper.

REMEMBER TO—

❑ write about a famous person you would like to meet

❑ make sure that every sentence helps make your composition more complete and that your ideas are presented in a logical order

❑ include details to help the reader understand what you are saying

❑ check your spelling, capitalization, ⋯⋯⋯ punctuation, and grammar carefully

Make sure that you have used subject and object pronouns correctly.

Name_____ Date_____

REVIEW

Text Structure: Cause and Effect

Text structure is the way a writer organizes his or her ideas. Studying the text structure can help you determine the relationships among ideas. Sometimes ideas in a text may have a **cause and effect** relationship.

Cause and effect questions ask why someone did something or why someone felt a certain way. Cause and effect questions may also ask why something happened.

To answer a cause and effect question, scan the story for the information requested in the question. Reread that part of the story carefully. Ask yourself questions such as these:

- Why did this character feel or behave this way?

- Why did this event happen in the way it did?

Read the paragraph. Then answer the questions that follow.

For as long as Mariana could remember, the old wooden shed had stood in her backyard. Each summer, she and her friends played around it, and year after year groundhogs made their homes beneath it. Then, one day, there was a great storm. Gale winds blew all night long. The next morning, when Mariana looked out her window, she saw the shed lying in hundreds of splintered pieces all over the ground. Although Mariana felt sad, she fondly remembered all the times she and her friends had played hide-and-go-seek around that rickety old shed.

1 **Cause:** Why did the shed collapse?

_____

2 **Effect:** How did Mariana feel about what happened to the shed?

_____

_____

Name Emilio Caceres   Date

 PRACTICE

Text Structure: Cause and Effect

Read the selection. Then read each question that follows the selection. Decide which is the best answer to each question. Mark the letter for that answer.

Science Quarterly

A Magazine for Young People

FALL 2002

El Niño

1   What determines the weather? Air currents, water temperature, and terrain play major roles. For some parts of the world, the phenomenon known as El Niño can also play a big role.

2   Usually, strong winds blow from east to west along the equator in the Pacific Ocean. This piles up water in the western Pacific. In the eastern Pacific, near California for instance, deeper water (which is colder than the sun-warmed surface water) gets pulled up from below to replace the water pushed west. So, the **normal** situation is warm water in the western Pacific Ocean, cold in the eastern Pacific Ocean.

3   In an El Niño, the winds pushing that water around get weaker. As a result, some of the warm water piled up in the western Pacific Ocean slumps back down to the eastern Pacific coastline, and not as much cold water gets pulled up from below. Both occurrences tend to make the water in the eastern Pacific Ocean *warmer*, which is one sign of an El Niño.

4   But it doesn't stop there. The warmer ocean then makes the winds weaker! If the winds get weaker, then the ocean gets warmer, which makes the winds get weaker, which makes the ocean get warmer. This cycle, an example of *positive feedback*, makes an El Niño grow.

continued on next page

Name Emilio Cáceres   **Date**

El Niño, *continued*

5   An El Niño warming of the eastern Pacific Ocean happens every two to seven years, causing major weather changes around the globe. In the United States, for example, the weather in Texas and other southern states usually becomes much wetter than normal. The Pacific Northwest states such as Oregon tend to be drier than normal.

6   In the spring of 1997, an El Niño produced disturbing weather conditions in many areas. Unusually strong tornadoes took place in Arkansas, Mississippi, and Tennessee, as did severe flooding from Texas to West Virginia. A deadly combination of heavy snow and rain, a rapid snowmelt, and ice jams occurred on North Dakota's Red River. The resulting floods broke records in the northern plains. A rare, devastating Force 5 tornado hit suburban Jarrell in central Texas on May 27, 1997.

7   During an El Niño, the air pressure over the warm water is low, which causes tropical winds to shift direction. When the winds shift towards the warm waters, they bring clouds full of moisture.

8   Giant rain clouds form over the warm water. Storms come ashore on every nearby coast. Heavy rains make rivers overflow. The rainwater quickly weakens hillsides. Landslides occur, destroying roads and houses.

9   With the spring thaw, water pours down mountainsides. Rivers overflow and flood the surrounding valleys and plains.

10   Stormy weather travels from west to east, causing more flooding as it moves. Even areas far away are affected by this weather pattern.

11   Meanwhile, on the other side of the ocean, the water is colder than normal and there is less rainfall. The land becomes dry, and crops die. Sometimes, after extreme dry weather, forest fires break out.

12   Then, after about a year, the ocean returns to its normal temperature. For the next few years, weather patterns are normal. Eventually, however, another warming trend begins.

13   Scientists are not sure what triggers an El Niño. This weather pattern appears to be cyclical, however. Scientists hope someday to be able to predict in what years an El Niño will occur. This will help people prepare for it.

Severe typhoons can occur during an El Niño.

Name_____ Date_____

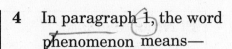

1 What happens in an El Niño to cause heavy rains? P.4

   A The ocean is colder than normal.

   B Snow builds up on mountain slopes. ✗

   C The ocean returns to its normal temperature. ✗

   D Giant rain clouds form over the warm water. ✗

2 What is the weather like in Texas during an El Niño? P.5

   A It is drier than normal. ✗

   B It is wetter than normal.

   C It is colder than normal. ✗

   D It is hotter than normal. ✗

3 What happens in an El Niño to cause floods?

P.6

   A Giant rain clouds form over cold water. ✗

   B Rainwater weakens hillsides. ✗

   C Huge forest fires break out. ✗

   D Heavy rains make rivers overflow.

4 In paragraph 1, the word phenomenon means—

   A an event

   B a place ✗

   C an outstanding young athlete ✗

   D an error ✗

P.1

5 What happens in an El Niño to cause landslides?

   A The heavy rains weaken hillsides.

   B The cold water causes dry conditions.

   C The winds shift towards the warm water.

   D Forest fires break out.

6 What happens during an El Niño to cause forest fires?

   A Fewer clouds form over the cold water, so there is less rainfall.

   B Stormy weather travels from east to west.

   C Winds blow towards the warm water.

   D Landslides destroy roads and houses.

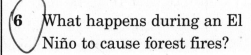

© Macmillan/McGraw-Hill

Name_____ Date_____

7 In paragraph 8, the word <u>coast</u> means—

   A   to move along the side

   B   to slide or glide along

   C   the land near the shoreline

   D   to slide down a hill

8 This selection is mainly about—

   A   how forest fires are caused during dry seasons

   B   how houses and roads can be destroyed by landslides

   C   the effect of warmer ocean waters on the weather patterns of the world

   D   how cold waters change wind patterns

9 According to the selection, how long does an El Niño usually last?

   A   About a year

   B   Two years

   C   Two to seven years

   D   About six months

10 Look at this diagram with information from the selection.

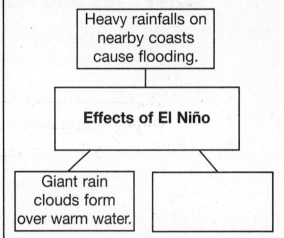

Which of the following belongs in the empty box?

   A   Landslides caused by heavy rains destroy houses and roads.

   B   Hurricanes are formed by high winds over warm waters.

   C   Ocean life is destroyed all over the world.

   D   Heavy snowstorms damage mountainsides.

Name Emilio Cáceres   **Date** 3-1-10

REVIEW

Adjectives and Adverbs

An **adjective** describes a noun or pronoun. It tells *what kind, which one,* or *how many*. Adjectives can compare things.

- Add *-er* to most adjectives to compare two things.

    Jack is <u>taller</u> than Aaron.

- Use *more* with long adjectives to compare two things.

    Vanilla ice cream is <u>more popular</u> than chocolate.

- Add *-est* to most adjectives to compare three or more things.

    An-mei is the <u>tallest</u> girl in our class.

- Use *most* with long adjectives to compare three or more things.

    That's the <u>most interesting</u> story I've heard in a long time!

An **adverb** usually describes verbs. Adverbs tell *how, when,* or *where*.

    Tomás raced <u>yesterday</u>. My dog can run <u>quickly</u>.

Write the form of the word in parentheses that BEST completes each sentence.

1. My bike is (small) than your bike.

    My bike is smaller than your bike.

2. That is the (beautiful) painting I've ever seen!

    That is the most beutiful painting I've ever seen!

3. That turtle moves (slow).

    That turtle move slowly.

4. Cherylynn is the (young) girl on our team.

    Cherylynn is the youngest girl on our team

Name Emilio Caceres   **Date** 3-1-10

TAKS PRACTICE 90

Adjectives and Adverbs

LaTrelle is a fourth grader. She is writing a paper about how her friend Susan got her first pet. Read her paper and try to think of improvements she might make. Then answer the questions that follow.

Lost and Found

(1) On Saturday morning Susan ate her breakfast quick. (2) This was the day she helped her father with the chores in the backyard. (3) It was her job to water the flowers and pull weeds. (4) Susan liked gardening. (5) Pulling weeds was hard work, but Susan did it happy. (6) When she finished weeding, she got out the watering can, filled it careful, and began to water the flowers by the back door.

(7) As Susan began to water the bushes farther away from the house, she thought she saw something out of the corner of her eye before it disappeared into the leaves. (8) "Was that a tiny furry tail?" Susan asked herself.

(9) Susan got down on her hands and knees, separated the branches of the bush, and looked closer. (10) Deep inside, she saw two yellow eyes, a pink nose, and white whiskers. (11) Then she heard a soft mewing cry. (12) "That's a kitten," Susan cried. (13) "I just know it's a kitten."

Name Emilio Caceres   **Date** 3-1-10

(14) Susan put out her hand and called quiet to the kitten. (15) A damp, orange and white, furry kitten slow crept toward her. (16) She picked up the kitten gently and held him. (17) Susan's heart began to beat faster. (18) He was the more beautiful kitten she had ever seen! (19) Her family had never had a dog or cat or fish or any other kind of animal or pet. (20) Susan really wanted a pet.

(21) Susan's father saw her with the kitten in her arms? (22) He looked for a collar or tag that showed who owned him, but there was none. (23) He put up flyers around town about the kitten, certain he was lost, but no one called.

(24) After two weeks, her mother said, (25) "Well, Susan, I guess the kitten doesn't have an owner."

(26) "Yes, he does," Susan said. (27) "Now he has us!"

---

1 What change, if any, should be made in sentence 1?

- **A** Change *quick* to **quickly**
- **B** Change *her* to **hers**
- **C** Change *breakfast* to **breakfust**
- **D** Make no change

S.1

2 What change, if any, should be made in sentence 5?

- **A** Change *was* to **were**
- **B** Change *happy* to **happily**
- **C** Change *happy* to **happier**
- **D** Make no change

S.5

© Macmillan/McGraw-Hill

Name _Emilio Cáceres_____ Date _3-1-10___

Emilio Cacaras

3 What change, if any, should be made in sentence 6?

A Change *careful* to **carefully**

B Change *began* to **beginned**

C Change *to* to **too**

D Make no change

4 What change, if any, should be made in sentence 8?

A Change *Was* to **Were**

B Change *tiny* to **tinily**

C Change the question mark after *tail* to a period

D Make no change

5 What change, if any, should be made in sentence 14?

A Change *quiet* to **quite**

B Change *quiet* to **quietly**

C Change the period after *kitten* to an exclamation mark

D Make no change

6 What change, if any, should be made in sentence 15?

A Change *A* to **a**

B Change *slow* to **slowly**

C Change *her* to **she**

D Make no change

7 What change, if any, should be made in sentence 18?

A Change *the* to **a**

B Change *more beautiful* to **most beautiful**

C Change *seen* to **seed**

D Make no change

Name_____ **Date**_____

8 What is the **BEST** way to rewrite the ideas in sentence 19?

  A Susan and her father never had no other kind of animal.

  B There had never been any kind of animal at Susan's house.

  C Her family had never had a pet of any kind.

  D Her family had never had a dog, or a cat, or a fish. Or any other kind of animal.

9 Which sentence could **BEST** be added after sentence 20?

  A They had already made flyers to try to find the kitten's owner.

  B The kitten closed his eyes and started to purr.

  C The garden was her father's pride and joy.

  D Susan liked horses very much.

10 What change, if any, should be made to sentence 21?

  A Change the question mark after *arms* to a period

  B Change *the kitten* to **it**

  C Change *Susan's* to **Susans'**

  D Make no change

Name_____ **Date**_____

 WRITE

Write about being an animal trainer and what you would teach
the animal you trained.

The box below will help you write your composition. Then, write your
composition on another piece of paper.

REMEMBER TO—

❏ write about being an animal trainer

❏ make sure to include details about what you
would like to teach your animal to do

❏ include vivid language to describe the
things you would teach your animal to do····

❏ try to use correct spelling, capitalization,
punctuation, grammar, and complete sentences

*Use adjectives
and adverbs in your
writing so that your
story is exciting
to read.*

Name_____ Date_____

REVIEW

Similarities and Differences

Sometimes you will be asked to name the ways in which the people or things that you read about are similar or different. To answer a question about similarities or differences, ask yourself:

- What is *alike* or *different* about the two characters, settings, or events mentioned in the question?

- What does one character do or say that the other does not?

- How is this character described at the beginning of the story, and how is the same character described at the end?

Read the paragraph. Then complete the chart comparing Pedro and Jerome that follows.

Pedro and Jerome were both fourth graders at Jefferson Elementary School. Both of them were good at math. They both also liked to play softball, but Pedro liked science fiction stories and Jerome preferred mysteries. Pedro went hiking on the weekends, while Jerome stayed home and did chores. Even though they were different in some ways, they were still good friends.

Similarities	Differences
1. Both are fourth graders.	1. Pedro liked science fiction stories
2. good at Math	2. But Jerome preferred
3. like softball	mysteries

© Macmillan/McGraw-Hill

When gathering or comparing information from different sources, remember that authors may organize their information in lists, charts, or diagrams.

Name_____ Date_____

 PRACTICE

Similarities and Differences

**Read the two selections. Then read each question that follows.
Decide which is the best answer to each question. Mark the letter
for that answer.**

*Amy and Maria are in the fourth grade. Their music teacher, Mr. Kraus,
thinks they are the most talented students in their class. He just asked
them if they would like to play a duet in the spring concert.*

From Amy's Diary

1   Today Mr. Kraus asked Maria and me to play a piece in the
spring concert. Ten fifth grade students will also be performing in
the concert. Maria and I will be the only duet and the only fourth
graders performing. Maria is excited about the concert, but I'm very
nervous. I have been taking flute lessons for two years but have
never played in front of an audience. I don't mind playing basketball
in front of a crowd, but playing my flute is different. I wish we were
playing basketball instead—that's something I know I'm good at!

2   My flute is silver and must be cleaned with a cleaning rod and
cloth after each use. It's such a pain to polish around those six
raised keys, and with all the practicing we'll be doing I'll be
polishing it a lot! Maria said she'd figure out a practice schedule for
us. I just hope Maria doesn't want to practice all the time. I have to
practice basketball, too. Maria says that many famous Americans
have played the flute, including George Washington, but today
I wish I'd never even seen one!

Name_____ **Date**_____

3   Maria and I looked through many sheets of music before we found a piece we both liked. It was hard finding something we could agree on. Maria is a much better musician than I am. At first, everything she liked was too hard for me. I think we'll sound great when we play the song we selected.

4   Tomorrow Maria and I will start practicing for the concert. Maria said we could rehearse at her grandmother's house after school. Her grandmother has a nice piano. I don't mind walking to her grandmother's house since my flute is very light and easy to carry.

From Maria's Diary

1   I can't believe it! Mr. Kraus asked Amy and me to play a duet in the spring concert. I can't wait—I love playing the piano in front of an audience. I wish the concert were tomorrow, instead of that basketball game. Playing in a concert is fun, but playing basketball is embarrassing. No matter how much I practice, I cannot score a point.

2   On the weekends and after school, I practice on my grandmother's baby grand piano. It is over five feet long and has 88 keys. It's huge! Amy said she didn't mind bringing her flute to Grandma's so that we could practice there. It'll be fun practicing together—I love spending time getting the music just right!

3   There is so much to do before the concert. This is just a partial list:

1. Make Amy a copy of the sheet music for the <u>piece</u> we decided to play at the concert.

2. Make a rehearsal schedule so that Amy and I can practice as often as possible.

3. Shop for a new dress to wear at the concert.

4. Make a list of family and friends to invite.

Name Emilio

Date 1-11-10

90

Use "From Amy's Diary" (pp. 113–114) to answer questions 1–3.

1 How are Amy and Maria different from the other students performing in the spring concert?

  A Amy and Maria are in third grade. The other students are in fourth grade.

  (B) Amy and Maria are in fourth grade and will play a duet. The other students are in fifth grade and will play solos or in groups.

  C Only Amy and Maria are nervous.

  D Amy and Maria are playing the piano. The other students are playing flutes.

2 How does Amy feel about playing in the concert?

  A Disappointed

  B Bored

  (C) Nervous

  D Excited

3 Why will Maria and Amy practice at Maria's grandmother's house?

  (A) Her house has a piano.

  B Her house is close to school.

  C Amy's flute might get damaged if she carries it.

  D Maria's grandmother will make sure they practice.

Use "From Maria's Diary" (p. 114) to answer questions 4–5.

4 In paragraph 3, the word <u>piece</u> means—

  A a part of a whole

  B a part in a board game

  (C) a musical selection

  D a painting or sculpture

5 How does Maria feel about playing in the concert?

  A Disappointed

  B Bored

  C Nervous

  (D) Excited

Name_____ **Date**_____

Use both "From Amy's Diary" (pp. 113–114) and "From Maria's Diary" (p. 114) to answer questions 6–10.

6 Amy and Maria are alike in that they both—

  A have younger sisters

  B like the music they selected

  C play the piano

  D hate performing in public

7 In what way are Amy and Maria different?

  A Maria plays the piano, but Amy plays the flute.

  B Maria plays the flute, but Amy plays the piano.

  C Maria plays soccer, but Amy plays basketball.

  D Maria plays basketball, but Amy plays soccer.

8 How is Amy's instrument different from Maria's?

  A Amy's instrument is too heavy to move, while Maria's instrument is light.

  B Amy's instrument is light, while Maria's instrument is too heavy to move.

  C Amy's instrument is made of gold, but Maria's is made of silver.

  D They are not different at all.

9 How are the instruments alike?

  A Both have strings.

  B Both are made from wood.

  C Both have keys.

  D Both are five feet long.

10 How did Maria organize her information differently from Amy?

  A She created a list.

  B She was happy to play a duet in the concert.

  C She drew pictures.

  D She prepared an outline before writing.

Name __Emilia Cáceres__   Date __3-1-10__

REVIEW

Regular and Irregular Plurals

A noun names a person, place, thing, or idea. **Plural nouns** name more than one person, place, thing, or idea.

Rule	Examples
To form the plural of most nouns, add –s.	dogs, bells, cows
To form the plural of a noun ending with x, s, ch, sh, or ss, add –es.	boxes, branches, bushes, grasses
To form the plural of a noun ending with a consonant + y, change the y to i and add –es.	cities, parties
To form the plural of a noun ending in a vowel + y, add –s.	boys, keys
Some nouns have plural forms that do not end in -s or -es.	geese, cattle, children, people

Write the correct plural form for each sentence below.

1. Did you see the herd of (deer, deers) that ran across the road?

   __deer__

2. Please put your (dishs, dishes) in the sink after you leave the table.

   __dishes__

3. I planted flowers in my garden to attract (butterflys, butterflies).

   __butterflies__

4. My sister lost three (tooths, teeth) before she turned five.

   __teeth__

TEST-TAKING TIP   If you're not sure how to form the correct plural of a noun, say the plural form aloud to see if it sounds right.

Name Emilio Cácere   **Date** 3-1-10

PRACTICE

Regular and Irregular Plurals

Troy is a fourth grader. He is working on a story about his friend Kareem's talent for drawing. Read his first draft and think about improvements Troy might make. Then answer the questions that follow.

Kareem and the Drawing Kit

(1) Kareem sat in the standes as his older brother, Daquon, hit two doubles in a row. (2) Daquon was one of the stars of the boys' baseball team at Grover Cleveland High. (3) He was athletic, he always got good grades, and he always was invited to class partys. (4) Kareem wanted to be just like his older brother. (5) "I'd be happy," Kareem thought, "if I were good at just one thing. (6) Is that too much to ask?"

(7) When he returned home, Kareem looked for something to distract himself from his problems. (8) "My baseball card collection will take my mind off things," he thought. (9) Kareem looked for his cards in the closet. (10) While searching, he saw some boxs he had never seen before. (11) He opened one up and found an old drawing kit. (12) "I don't remember this," Kareem thought. (13) "It must belong to Daquon."

(14) Kareem started reading the directions in front of him.

(15) Before he knew it, he was making some sketchs on a sheet of paper.

(16) A picture of a flock of gooses began taking shape on the page.

Name _Emilio Cáceres_   Date _3-1-10_

(17) Suddenly he heard the door to his room open. (18) Daquon, he was back home from playing his game. (19) Kareem tried to hide his picture, but Daquon grabbed it away.

(20) "Did you draw this?" Daquon asked.

(21) "Yes," Kareem replied timidly, afraid that his brother would tease him.

(22) "It's really great!" said Daquon. (23) "You should definitely show this to Mom and Dad!"

(24) Kareem grinned. (25) Kareem thought, "Maybe I am good at something after all."

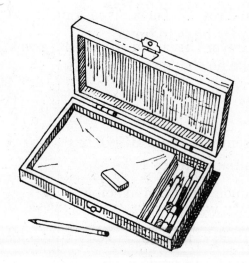

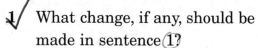

1 What change, if any, should be made in sentence 1?

   A Change *standes* to **stands**
   B Change *older* to **more old**
   C Change *doubles* to **doubls**
   D Make no change

   S.1

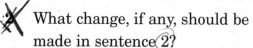

2 What change, if any, should be made in sentence 2?

   A Change *was* to **were**
   B Change *boys'* to **boys**
   C Change *High* to **high**
   D Make no change

   S.2

Name_____ Date_____

3 What change, if any, should be made in sentence 3?

A Change *grades* to *grades'*

B Change *got* to *get*

C Change *partys* to *parties*

D Make no change

4 What change, if any, should be made in sentence 10?

A Change *saw* to *sees*

B Change *boxs* to *boxes*

C Change *boxs* to *boxs'*

D Make no change

5 Which sentence could **BEST** be added after sentence 13?

A Daquon often stored some of his extra things in Kareem's closet.

B Daquon collected baseball cards, too.

C Daquon's baseball card collection was bigger than Kareem's.

D Daquon drew a map for a social studies project.

6 What change, if any, should be made in sentence 15?

A Change *directions* to *directiones*

B Change *began* to *begin*

C Change *sketchs* to *sketches*

D Make no change

7 What change, if any, should be made in sentence 16?

A Change *A* to *a*

B Change *flock* to *flocks*

C Change *gooses* to *geese*

D Make no change

8 What is the **BEST** way to rewrite the ideas in sentence 18?

A Daquon, was he back from his game?

B Daquon was back from his game.

C Daquon back home from his game.

D Daquon was back home from the game he was playing.

© Macmillan/McGraw-Hill

Name_____ Date_____

9 What change, if any, should be made in sentence 22?

    A Change the exclamation mark after *great* to a period

    B Change *really* to **real**

    C Change *Daquon* to **him**

    D Make no change

    S.22

10 What is the **BEST** way to combine the ideas in sentences 24 and 25?

    A Kareem grinned and thought, "Maybe I am good at something after all."

    B Kareem grinned as he had a pleasant thought.

    C "Maybe I am good at something after all," Kareem grinned and thought.

    D Kareem grinned, thought, and said, "Maybe I am good at something."

S.24&25

Name_____ **Date**_____

 WRITE

Write a composition that tells how you would raise money for your school and what it should be spent on.

The box below will help you write your composition. Then, write your composition on another piece of paper.

REMEMBER TO—

- ☐ write about how you will raise money for your school

- ☐ make sure to include details about what you want to buy with the money you raise

- ☐ include vivid language to explain why your school needs the items you want to buy

- ☐ try to use correct spelling, capitalization, punctuation, grammar, and sentences

Look at your nouns. Did you form plurals correctly?

Name Emilio Cáceres   Date 9 – 6 – 10

REVIEW

Representing Information

Outlines organize information into main ideas and supporting details. **Graphic organizers**, such as word webs, also organize information into topics and details.

Read the passage. Then complete the outline that follows.

Cowboy

My dog, Cowboy, is the smartest dog I know. He can do lots of tricks. One trick he can do is to sit. I just tell him once, and he does it! Cowboy also knows how to roll over. He just learned how to speak, or bark on command. My brother also taught him how to "do a doughnut," which means he turns around in a circle. I'm really proud of my dog.

Cowboy is also very protective. When my baby sister tries to crawl into dangerous places, he blocks her with his body. He also barks loudly when a stranger comes to the door. No one can get past him without my hearing about it! He also sleeps by my door at night, just to make sure I'm safe.

I. Cowboy can do tricks.	II. Cowboy is very protective.
A. Cowboy can sit	A. he blocks baby sister to going in dangerous places
B. knows how to roll over	
C. Speak or bark on command	B. barks loudly to strangers
D. turns around in a circle	C. Protect cow asleep

TEST-TAKING TIP

Writers usually keep related ideas together. To fill in an organizer, first identify the main idea of each paragraph, and then list the supporting details.

Name Emilio Cáceres   **Date** 12-06-10

PRACTICE

Representing Information

Read the selection. Then read each question that follows the selection. Decide which is the best answer to each question. Mark the letter for that answer.

Polar Bears

1   Polar bears are survivors. They live near the Arctic Ocean, where temperatures can fall below −50°F for many days in a row. Strong winds can make it seem even colder. The land is barren and frozen. Snow and ice cover the ground for much of the year. The Arctic Ocean is frigid and filled with chunks of floating ice. During winter, the sun sets in October and does not rise again until almost March.

2   Polar bears are excellent hunters. They most often hunt ringed seals. To do so, they wait by the breathing holes of the seals and snatch the seals as they come up for air. When seals are scarce, polar bears hunt small birds, rodents, and reindeer. They also crack ice to catch fish in the waters below. On land, they can reach speeds of 25 miles per hour. Their keen sense of smell helps them track their prey. They can smell a seal from more than 20 miles away!

3   The polar bear's body protects it from the harsh Arctic environment. Its fur helps it blend in with the snow-covered surroundings. The polar bear has two layers of water-repellent fur. A thick layer of blubber, or fat, is underneath the fur. It helps to block out the cold. A polar bear's furry, webbed feet can be a foot wide. Its feet help it stay warm and swim fast. Its small, compact ears and tail help prevent heat from leaving its body.

Name Emilio Cáceres   **Date** 12-06-10

#5

4   Polar bears conserve energy they need to stay warm by sleeping. Polar bears spend seven to eight hours a day sleeping. They usually sleep during the day and hunt at night when seals are more active. On warm days, they will sleep on their backs with their feet in the air. On very cold days, they dig into the snow, forming small caves for shelter. Polar bears always sleep with their backs or sides to the wind. When a bad storm hits, they roll up into a ball and cover their noses to keep warm. Polar bears can stay like this for days.

5   Female polar bears usually give birth to two cubs between November and January. Just before giving birth, a pregnant polar bear may weigh 1,100 pounds. Cubs are born with their eyes closed and weigh 1 to $1\frac{1}{2}$ pounds. By the time cubs are ready to leave the den in late March, they weigh between 22 and 33 pounds. Mother bears are very protective of their young and care for their cubs until they are over two years old.

6   The Inuit, a Native American group in the Arctic, used to hunt polar bears. They would eat the polar bear's meat and use the fur to make clothing. They would use almost every part of the bear. Today, hunting is still the most common cause of death in polar bears. Before a 1973 ban, hunters used airplanes, snowmobiles, and boats to hunt polar bears. Efforts are now being made to protect polar bears. It would be sad if this unique animal were to disappear from the planet.

Name_____ Date_____

1 Look at this outline of information from paragraph 1.

> **I.** Arctic environment
>
> **A.** Temperatures fall below –50˚F.
>
> **B.** Snow and ice cover the ground for many months.
>
> **C.** _____
>
> **D.** There's no sunlight during winter.

Which fact goes in the blank?

A Polar bears are survivors.

B Polar bears hunt seals.

C The Arctic Ocean is frigid and filled with ice chunks.

D Polar bears sleep a lot.

P.1

2 Look at this diagram of information from paragraph 2.

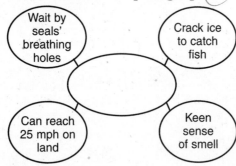

Which completes the diagram?

A Polar bears are good hunters.

B Arctic weather is harsh.

C Polar bears care for their cubs.

D Polar bears have thick fur.

P.2

3 Look at this outline of information from paragraph 3.

> **I.** Polar bear's body protects it from environment.
>
> **A.** Fur blends in with snow.
>
> **B.** Water-repellent fur keeps skin dry.
>
> **C.** _____
>
> **D.** Furry, webbed feet make it fast swimmer.
>
> **E.** Small ears and tail help keep heat in.

Which fact goes in the blank?

A Snow covers surroundings.

B Blubber blocks out cold.

C Blubber is also called fat.

D Short fur helps bear run.

P.3

4 Which of these best describes the author's attitude about polar bears?

A Admiration

B Fear

C Amusement

D Dislike

© Macmillan/McGraw-Hill

Name_____ Date_____

5 Look at this chart of information from paragraph 4.

CAUSE	EFFECTS
Weather is cold and stormy.	1. Polar bear digs into snow to form a cave.
	2. Polar bear rolls into a ball.
	3. Polar bear remains rolled into a ball for several days.
	4. _____

Which fact goes in the blank?

A Polar bear sleeps on back.

B Polar bear hunts reindeer.

C Polar bear sleeps at night.

D Polar bear covers nose with paws.

6 According to the article, what may weigh 1,100 pounds?

A Female polar bears when they are pregnant

B Polar bear cubs at birth

C Male polar bears

D Polar bear cubs when they are ready to leave the den

7 In paragraph 1, the word row means—

A to propel a boat with oars

B a line of seats

C without a break in time

D a line of houses

8 This passage is mostly about—

A how polar bears raise their young

B how polar bears catch their food

C where polar bears live

D the many ways polar bears survive

© Macmillan/McGraw-Hill

Name_____ **Date**_____

REVIEW

Using Apostrophes and Commas

Two types of commonly used punctuation are **commas** and **apostrophes**. Look at the rules below for using them.

Rules	Examples
Use **commas** to separate items in a series, or list, of three or more items. Put a comma after each item in the series except for the last item. Use *and* or *or* before the last item.	I bought bread, milk, apples, and carrots at the store.
Use a **comma** to set off the name of a person who is addressed directly.	Marco, would you please pass the green beans?
Use an **apostrophe** in a contraction to represent the letters that are left out when words are combined.	Do not = Don't Could not = Couldn't (The apostrophe replaces *o*.)
Use an **apostrophe** to show possession or ownership. Add *'s* to a word to show possession.	The book belongs to Carl. It is Carl's book. The bike belongs to Chris. It is Chris's bike.

Add commas and apostrophes to the sentences as needed.

1 LaDonna have you finished your homework?

2 Lucass mom sent a sandwich an apple and some celery for his lunch.

3 Jacob doesnt know that his friend cant swim.

Name Emilio Cáceres   **Date** _____

PRACTICE

Using Apostrophes and Commas

Grace is a fourth grader at Steiner Elementary School. She is writing a story about her first plane ride. Read her story and look for ways she might improve it. Then answer the questions that follow.

Flying to Laredo

(1) My first airplane ride was very exciting. (2) It was so exciting, actually, that I thought it might be my last flight!

(3) My parents and I were flying to Laredo to visit my Aunt Helen and my cousin Eric my cousin Teresa and my cousin Adam. (4) When we arrived at the airport, we couldnt find a place to park. (5) My dad drove around, looking for a parking place, until I thought we were going to miss our flight. (6) Finally, we found a parking spot, and we raced into the airport.

(7) After we got to the ticket counter, my dad realized we had left my moms suitcase by the car. (8) He rushed back, found the bag, and raced back to the counter. (9) "Youre sure huffing and puffing, Dad!" I said.

(10) "Grace, I'm glad you think this is funny," he said, and he said it with a grin. (11) "I sure don't!"

(12) Finally, it was time to board the plane. (13) As we took off, I felt my stomach jump. (14) "Wow! What a strange feeling!" I thought as I watched the cars below me get smaller and smaller.

Name_____ Date_____

(15) About an hour into the flight, the plane started bumping and rolling. (16) My juice chips and fruit went flying. (17) My heart started beating faster.

(18) "Mom what is happening?" I asked nervously.

(19) "Just a little bumpy. (20) There's nothing to be anxious about," she replied.

(21) We bounced around in the rough sky for what seemed like hours.

(22) Everyone else on the plane seemed calm, but I felt really scared.

(23) I was overjoyed when the plane's wheels finally touched the ground.

(24) I hope my next flight is easier than my first one!

1   Which is the **BEST** way to revise sentence 3?

   A My parents and I were flying to Laredo to visit my Aunt Helen and my cousin Eric, my cousin Teresa, and my cousin Adam.

   B My parents and I were flying to Laredo to visit my Aunt Helen, Eric, Teresa, and Adam.

   C My parents and I were flying to Laredo to visit my Aunt Helen and my cousins Eric, Teresa, and Adam.

   D No revision is needed.

2   What change, if any, should be made in sentence 4?

   A Change the comma after *airport* to a period

   B Change *find* to **fine**

   C Change *couldnt* to **couldn't**

   D Make no change

Name_____ Date_____

3 What change, if any, should be made in sentence 7?

   A Change *my dad* to **My Dad**

   B Change *moms* to **mom's**

   C Change *left* to **leaved**

   D Make no change

4 What change, if any, should be made in sentence 9?

   A Change *Youre* to **Your**

   B Change *Youre* to **You're**

   C Remove the comma after *puffing*

   D Make no change

5 Which is the **BEST** way to revise sentence 10?

   A "Grace, I'm glad. You think this is funny," he said and said with a grin.

   B "Grace, I'm glad you think this is funny," he said it with a grin.

   C "Grace, I'm glad you think this is funny," he said with a grin.

   D No revision is needed.

6 Which sentence could **BEST** be added after sentence 14?

   A I tried to relax but couldn't.

   B My dad's car is small.

   C It was a small plane.

   D My mom travels a lot.

7 Which change, if any, should be made in sentence 16?

   A Add a comma after *juice* and after *chips*

   B Change *fruit* to **frute**

   C Change *went* to **goes**

   D Make no change

8 What change, if any, should be made in sentence 18?

   A Change the question mark after *happening* to an exclamation mark

   B Add a comma after *Mom*

   C Change *nervously* to **nervous**

   D Make no change

Name_____ **Date**_____

9 What change, if any, should be made in sentence 23?

   A Change *plane's* to **planes'**

   B Change *overjoyed* to **overjoied**

   C Change *wheels* to **wheels'**

   D Make no change

10 Which of the following is **NOT** a complete sentence?

   A Sentence 1

   B Sentence 9

   C Sentence 18

   D Sentence 19

Name_____ Date_____

 WRITE

> Write a composition about the first time you did something new.

The box below will help you write your composition. Then write your composition on another piece of paper.

REMEMBER TO—

- ❏ describe the first time you did something new

- ❏ include details about how you felt during your new experience

- ❏ include vivid language so your reader can imagine how you felt during this experience

- ❏ check for correct spelling, capitalization, punctuation, grammar, and sentences

Did you use commas and apostrophes correctly?

Name Emilio Cáceres   **Date** 1-07-10

REVIEW

Critical Reading

Some questions on the TAKS test will ask you to support your answers. You can use information from the title, the story, or the illustrations to support your answers.

Read the passage. Then answer the questions that follow.

Little Brother's Mistake

Lindsey stormed into the house and slammed the door. She threw her backpack on the table and flopped into a chair at the kitchen table.

"What's wrong, Lindsey?" her mom asked.

Before Lindsey could answer, her brother Corbin opened the door and poked his head in. He looked at Lindsey with a worried frown and then came in slowly, hanging his head.

1   How is Lindsey feeling?

She was feeling mad.

What information from the story did you use to answer this?

Lindsey stormed into the house and slammed the door

2   Why do you think Lindsey is feeling that way?

Maybe her little brother broke something that is hers

What information from the story did you use to answer this?

he looked at lindsey with a worried frown.

Name Emilio Cáceres **Date** 1-07-10

TAKS PRACTICE

Critical Reading

Read the selection. Then read each question that follows the selection. Decide which is the best answer to each question. Mark the letter for that answer.

Jerome's First Race

1   When the alarm went off, Jerome jumped out of bed. His stomach started doing back-flips as he got dressed. He could barely tie his shoes. He went down the hall to the kitchen. When he sat down at the kitchen table, his mother asked, "What would you like for breakfast?"

2   "Nothing, Mom. I don't think I could eat a bite!" Jerome answered.

3   "You've got to eat something, Jerome. You need lots of energy today," his mother said as she placed a glass of orange juice in front of him. All Jerome could think about was how hard it was to get to sleep last night. Worse than that was the restless sleep he had gotten. Jerome had awakened several times after having strange dreams. He had looked under his bed twice during the night to see if his team shoes and uniform were still in the gym bag where he had left them.

4   Jerome drank the juice, choked down a bowl of cereal, and then went outside to wait for Kai's mom to pick him up. He paced around the driveway, back and forth, until his mom finally called to him, "You'd better sit down and wait quietly, or you'll wear yourself out!" He tried to sit still but was up and pacing only seconds after he had sat on the steps.

5   After what seemed like an eternity, Kai's mom drove up in the van, and Jerome climbed into the backseat. He greeted his teammate, but Kai didn't answer. Jerome looked at Kai and thought he looked a bit pale. Then Kai reached out to help Jerome with his gym bag. Jerome noticed that Kai's hand was shaking.

6   "Are you okay, Kai?" Jerome asked.

© Macmillan/McGraw-Hill

Name_____ **Date**_____

7   "Yeah, I'm fine," Kai replied, but his voice sounded a little shaky. He stared out the window and anxiously plucked at the sleeve of his jacket. "I didn't sleep very well last night."

8   "Me either," whispered Jerome.

9   "Will you two just relax!" cried Kai's mother. "You are both more than ready for today."

10   When the boys got to school, they headed for the gym to put on their uniforms. Kai and Jerome were silent as they walked across the gym on their way to the locker room.

11   The coach, noticing how serious the boys looked, stopped them and said, "Don't worry, boys. You've trained hard, and I know you'll do well. Just relax and do your best."

12   In the locker room, several of the older boys on the team were laughing and joking around. As he put on his running shoes, Jerome's heart slowed down, and he started to smile. As he slipped on his shorts and jersey, he felt the tension that had been building up all night finally begin to melt away. He wished he had talked with his coach sooner. It was simple—really all so simple. "Coach is right!" he thought to himself. "All I need to do is my best." Why hadn't he thought of this before?

13   Jerome turned and looked at Kai. The color was returning to his face, and his hands weren't shaking anymore. Kai smiled at Jerome and said, "I guess this is it!"

14   "It sure is," answered Jerome. "Let's go have some fun!"

15   Kai laughed, then shouted, "On your mark. Get set. Go!"

Name_____   Date_____

1 Which of these best describes how Jerome <u>felt when</u> he woke up?

   A Angry

   C Nervous? P.2

   B Happy

   D Curious

2 Which of these sentences from the story shows the reader how Jerome is feeling at the beginning?

   A *When the alarm went off, Jerome jumped out of bed.*

   B *His stomach started doing back-flips as he got dressed.*

   C *He went down the hall to the kitchen.*

   D *When the boys got to school, they headed for the gym to put on their uniforms.*

P.1

3 Where was Jerome going that morning?

   A To a spelling bee

   B To Kai's house

   C To a track meet? P.12

   D To a basketball game

4 Which part of the story shows where Jerome was going?

   A The title ?

   B Paragraph 1

   C Paragraph 4

   D Paragraph 5

5 Which of these best describes how Kai felt when Jerome got into the car?

   A Jealous

   B Bored

   C Excited

   D Nervous? P.5

6 Which sentence from the story shows the reader how Kai was feeling?

   A *Kai's mom drove up in the van, and Jerome climbed into the backseat.*

   B *Then Kai reached out to help Jerome with his gym bag.*

   C *Jerome noticed that Kai's hand was shaking.*

   D *"Are you okay, Kai?" Jerome asked.*

P.6

© Macmillan/McGraw-Hill

Name_____ Date_____

7 Which of these best describes how the boys felt after their coach talked to them?

   A Scared

   B Shy

   C Even more worried

   D More relaxed

P.11

8 Which sentence from the story shows the reader how the boys were feeling after they talk with the coach?

   A *"Yeah, I'm fine," Kai replied, but his voice sounded a little shaky.*

   B *When the boys got to school, they headed for the gym to put on their uniforms.*

   C *"You've trained hard, and I know you'll do well."*

   D *As he put on his running shoes, Jerome's heart slowed down, and he started to smile.*

9 Which statement is true of both Kai and Jerome?

   A They are both too nervous to eat.

   B Both boys are annoyed with their mothers.

   C Both boys are nervous before running in their first race.

   D They are both anxious to win.

10 Where was the race being held?

   A At school

   B At the park

   C Around the pool

   D At Kai's house

© Macmillan/McGraw-Hill

Name_____ Date_____

REVIEW

Sentence Punctuation

A **sentence** is a group of words that makes up a complete thought. It begins with a capital letter and ends with a period, a question mark, or an exclamation mark.

There are four kinds of sentences.

- A sentence that tells something is called a **statement**. A statement ends in a period.

- A sentence that asks something is called a **question**. A question ends in a question mark.

- A sentence that tells someone to do something is called a **command**. A command ends in a period.

- A sentence that shows strong feeling is an **exclamation**. An exclamation ends in an exclamation mark.

Complete the exercises below. Mark each sentence with the correct punctuation.

1 Jane is going to the store __.__

   This sentence is a(n) _____.

2 Did you forget your shopping list _?_

   This sentence is a(n) _____.

3 What a terrific omelet this is _!_

   This sentence is a(n) _____.

Name_____ **Date**_____

PRACTICE

Sentence Punctuation

Cliff is a fourth grader at Lake Travis Elementary School. Read his story about a stormy night and think about ways in which he might make improvements. Then answer the questions that follow.

A Rainy Game Night

(1) Rivers of water were pouring down the windows of our school bus. (2) The windshield wipers were working furiously, but they couldn't keep up with the rain. (3) The bus had slowed to a crawl because the driver couldn't see the road in front of him? (4) I was worried. (5) I knew that if the driver went too fast on a wet road, the bus might be in an accident. (6) My dad had a small accident at work last year.

(7) Suddenly, there was a flash of lightning. (8) A few seconds later, I heard a loud crash of thunder. (9) "Oh, no," I thought to myself. (10) "The storm sounds like it's right on top of us."

(11) Then, just as suddenly as it started, the rain stopped. (12) The sky began to clear. (13) I could see the lights of Plainville off to the right. (14) I asked my coach, "What time is it." (15) He looked at his watch and said, "It's 6:50 P.M. (16) We're just in time for the game."

(17) "Wow," I said to my friend Jack, "we were only in that rainstorm for twenty minutes. (18) Didn't it seem like a lot longer."

Name_____ Date_____

(19) At 6:55 P.M., the bus pulled up to the gymnasium to let the team off. (20) We rushed to the locker room to get dressed. (21) Our coach stood up in the locker room and said, "I know that was a pretty scary storm, but dont let it bother you. (22) It's game time now. (23) Are you ready to play?"

(24) "You bet!" we all shouted. (25) We raced out to the court, ready for the game. (26) We all played our best, and we beat them by 18 points. (27) It was our best game all season.

1   What change, if any, should be made in sentence 3?

   A   Change *couldn't* to **couldnt'**

   B   Change *slowed* to **slowly**

   C   Change the question mark after *him* to a period

   D   Make no change

2   Which sentence does **NOT** belong in the first paragraph?

   A   Sentence 1

   B   Sentence 3

   C   Sentence 4

   D   Sentence 6

Name_____ **Date**_____

3 Which sentence can **BEST** be added after sentence 8?

  A The coach said we had a good chance of winning.

  B You can tell how far away a lightning strike is by how long it takes for the thunder to be heard.

  C Plainville is a small town, about 20 miles from my house.

  D All the players scrambled to get into their uniforms.

4 What change, if any, should be made in sentence 9?

  A Change *thought* to **thinks**

  B Change the period after *myself* to a question mark

  C Change *myself* to **me**

  D Make no change

5 What is the **BEST** way to combine sentences 12 and 13?

  A The sky began to clear, and I could see the lights of Plainville off to the right.

  B The sky began to clear but I could see the lights of Plainville off to the right.

  C The sky began to clear, I could see the lights of Plainville off to the right.

  D I could see the lights of Plainville off to the right in the clear sky.

6 What change, if any, should be made in sentence 14?

  A Change the period after *it* to a question mark

  B Change the period after *it* to a comma

  C Change *coach* to **coaches**

  D Make no change

Name_____ **Date**_____

7 What change, if any, should be made in sentence 18?

    A Change *Didn't* to **did'nt**

    B Change *seem* to **seems**

    C Change the period after *longer* to a question mark

    D Make no change

8 What change, if any, should be made in sentence 21?

    A Change *dont* to **don't**

    B Change *it* to **it's**

    C Change the period after *you* to a question mark

    D Make no change

9 The meaning of sentence 26 can be improved by changing *them* to—

    A the players

    B our players

    C the Plainville team

    D some friends

10 What change, if any, should be made in sentence 27?

    A Change *best* to **better**

    B Change *our* to **your**

    C Change the period after *season* to a question mark

    D Make no change

Name_____ Date_____

WRITE

Write about ways people can overcome their fears.

The box below will help you write your composition. Then write your composition on another piece of paper.

REMEMBER TO—

❑ write about ways to overcome fears

❑ check that all your sentences support your central idea

❑ use words or phrases that make the writing interesting

❑ check for correct spelling, capitalization, punctuation, and grammar

Make sure to include different types of sentences.

Name _Emilio_   Date _1-11-10_

REVIEW

Understanding Purpose

Authors have a **purpose**, or reason, for writing. An author's purpose might be to persuade, to inform, or to entertain, or a combination of these. The words, setting, and other information an author uses can be clues to the author's purpose.

Read the selection. Then answer the questions that follow.

Gwen's Party

    Gwen invited her friends to an outdoor party at her house. The day before the party, she made cupcakes for her guests. Then she made colorful paper flowers for decorations. Gwen's dog, Bitsy, tried to eat one of the flowers.

    On the day of the party, Gwen set the cupcakes on the kitchen counter before going upstairs to get dressed. While she was upstairs, she heard a loud noise. She rushed downstairs to find cupcakes all over the kitchen floor. Bitsy was having a feast! She had a pink frosting mustache. Just then, Gwen heard the doorbell ring. Her guests had arrived.

    Gwen directed her friends to the backyard. Then she put Bitsy in the garage and cleaned up the mess. Just as she was joining her friends, big drops of rain started to fall.

    Gwen and her friends moved the party indoors, and everyone had a good time—even Gwen.

1   What is the author's purpose?

    To inform

2   What parts of the story are clues to the author's purpose?

    Gwen invited her friends to an outdoor party

Name Emilio Caceres.   **Date** 12-8-09.

TAKS PRACTICE

Understanding Purpose

Read the selection. Then read each question that follows the selection. Decide which is the best answer to each question. Mark the letter for that answer.

The Springfield Sun

February 14, 2002	Section A
Editorials	

Plant More Trees

1   In the past few years, our town has lost many of our lovely old elm trees. One after another, the trees have gotten sick and died. With so many elm trees gone, our town looks far more colorless and barren. It may be difficult to keep elm trees alive, but there are many other kinds of sturdy and beautiful trees.

2   There are many reasons why we should plant more trees in our town. To begin with, trees are beautiful. The budding leaves are a sign of spring. The springtime blossoms of pear, apple, and cherry trees are lovely and fragrant. More trees would make our town more attractive.

3   Another reason to plant trees is that they provide shade. Shade protects people and houses from the heat and glare of the sun. A house or building surrounded by trees would be cooled by the leafy branches. This would make it less necessary to turn on fans and air conditioners, and we would save energy. What would a picnic be like if trees did not shade the picnic tables? We need trees for the comfort they provide.

continued on next page

© Macmillan/McGraw-Hill

Name _Emilio C._   Date _12-08-09_

Plant More Trees, *continued*

4   Trees also provide shelter and food for wildlife. Birds nest in their branches. Bees make their hives in tree trunks. Squirrels and chipmunks eat the nuts and fruit that fall from the trees. These animals are an important part of our ecosystem. Without trees, they cannot survive.

5   Another very important reason for planting trees is that they are necessary for the environment. Without trees, we could not live. Trees absorb the carbon dioxide we exhale. They produce the oxygen we need to breathe. Trees have an important role in recycling water, too. The roots of trees store water from the soil. The trees then return some water to the atmosphere through their leaves.

6   Both National Arbor Day and Texas Arbor Day are celebrated on the last Friday of April. I am ashamed to say that we have much less to celebrate this year. Few elm trees remain, and nowhere in our town can you find even one pecan tree—our own state tree! Trees have always been basic to our needs, providing food, shelter, and fuel. Some have also stood watch over the lives and events that, woven together, represent the very fabric of our nation. These are the trees that grow at historic places, at birthplaces of America's historic figures, and at places where legendary events have occurred. The **National Register of Historic Trees** preserves our rich heritage for future generations, through the unique perspective of the living witnesses of our history.

7   In our town there must be more than one special tree that has stood as a witness to our history, under which town leaders gathered to sign treaties, plan the community, or mark key surveys. I propose that we find these trees and nominate them for the **National Register of Historic Trees**. This will give our community a wonderful opportunity to showcase our distinct heritage.

8   In addition, let's take better care of our older trees and set aside some of the town's budget for a tree-planting effort. Let's begin to plant new trees to mark special events and provide a better world for our children and our children's children. The money we spend will serve our community for years to come. We owe it to our town and the generations to come!

Name Emilio C. Date 12-08-09

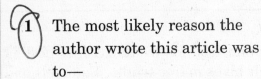

1 The most likely reason the author wrote this article was to—

A persuade the town government to plant trees

B describe the trees in town

C explain water conservation

D remind the townspeople that animals need shelter

2 In paragraph 1, the word barren means—

A shady

B lifeless

C dry

D beautiful

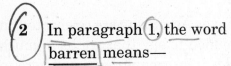

3 The author organizes paragraphs 2 through 5 by—

A describing how the town's trees were destroyed

B giving reasons why planting trees would be good for the town

C explaining how trees would brighten up the town

D discussing the trees best suited to the climate

4 Why did the writer's town lose so many of its trees?

A The trees were cut down to allow for more sunshine.

B The trees died from disease.

C The trees were torn up by tornadoes.

D The trees were chopped down by loggers.

5 Which statement is true of both people and trees?

A They make carbon dioxide.

B They like the shade.

C They bud in spring.

D They use the air to survive.

6 According to the article, trees help wildlife by—

A providing food and shelter

B providing hiding places for squirrels and insects

C controlling noise pollution by absorbing sound

D keeping the soil from being blown away by the wind

© Macmillan/McGraw-Hill

Name _Emilio C._   Date _2-08-09_

7 Look at this diagram of information from paragraph 4.

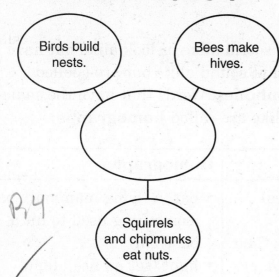

R.4

Which idea belongs in the empty circle?

(A) How trees help wildlife ?

B How trees recycle ✗

C How trees help people

D Why plant more trees ✗

8 This article is mainly about—

A why the elm trees died ?

B why the townspeople should increase their taxes

C the National Register of Historic Trees ✗

D why the townspeople should plant more trees ✗

9 Look at this outline of information from paragraph 5.

> **I.** Good for the environment
>
> **A.** Absorb carbon dioxide
>
> **B.** Produce oxygen
>
> **C.** _____

Which information belongs in the blank?

A Absorb sound ✗

B Recycle water ?

C Return carbon dioxide to the atmosphere ✗

D Stop wind from blowing away soil ✗

10 Why does the writer think the town should nominate trees for the **National Register of Historic Trees?**

A The town would be famous. ✗

B The trees would remind people of the town's heritage. ✗

P.6

C Registering a tree is free. ✗

D The organization would help pay for planting trees.

Name_____ Date_____

REVIEW

Homonyms

Homonyms are words that sound alike or look alike but have different meanings. Words that sound alike but are spelled differently are called **homophones**. Words that have the same spellings and often sound alike are called **homographs**.

Homophones	Homographs
• choose (pick); chews (bites) • there (place); they're (contraction for *they are*); their (possessive pronoun for *they*) • plane (a vehicle that flies and carries passengers); plain (simple)	• bat (a flying mammal); bat (something used to hit a baseball) • light (set on fire); light (shine brightly) • drop (let go); drop (a tiny amount)

Circle the correct word to complete each sentence below.

1   My little brother yelled, "Can I come (too, to, two)?"

2   My muscles are (soar, sore) after exercising yesterday.

3   Please (weight, wait) for me after school.

4   For my birthday we ate (steak, stake), green beans, and mashed potatoes.

5   "(There, Their) are many (plains, planes) to (chews, choose) from in our toy department," bragged the manager of the store.

TEST-TAKING TIP   If you don't know the meaning of a word on a test, use the words and phrases in the same paragraph as context clues. They will help you make a good guess.

© Macmillan/McGraw-Hill

Name _Emilio Cáceres_   **Date** _12-11-09_

TAKS PRACTICE

Homonyms

Danté, a fourth grader at Barbara Jordan Elementary School, is writing a report about the solar system for his science class. Read his report. Think about corrections he might make. Then answer the questions that follow.

The Solar System

(1) Look in the night sky on a clear night. (2) You can see twinkling stars. (3) You can see other bright objects, to. (4) They shine with a steady light. (5) They reflect the light of the Sun. (6) They are planets like Earth.

(7) The Sun and the planets make up the solar system. (8) The Sun is the bright star at the center. (9) Their are nine planets. (10) Each one travels around the Sun in a regular path. (11) The path is called an orbit. (12) The orbits are different distances from the Sun. (13) The closer a planet is to the Sun, the warmer it is. (14) The farther from the Sun it is, the colder it is.

(15) It takes time for a planet to go around the Sun. (16) Depends on how far the planet is from the Sun. (17) Four example, Earth goes around the Sun once every $365\frac{1}{4}$ days. (18) Mercury goes around the Sun once every 88 days.

Name_____ **Date**_____

(19) The planets nearer to the Sun are the "inner planets." (20) In order of distance from the Sun, the inner planets are Mercury, Venus, Earth, and Mars. (21) The inner planets are small. (22) They are made of solid rock.

(23) The planets farthest from the Sun are the "outer planets." (24) In order of distance from the Sun, the outer planets are Jupiter, Saturn, Uranus, Neptune, and Pluto. (25) Except for Pluto, the outer planets are huge. (26) They are made up mostly of gases such as hydrogen. (27) On Jupiter and Saturn, the swirling gases are read, orange, and yellow in color. (28) The gases on Uranus and Neptune are blue or blue-green in color.

Jupiter and its four largest moons (composite photo)

Name _____ **Date** _____

1. What change, if any, should be made in sentence 3?
   A Change *You* to *Your*
   B Change *see* to *seen*
   C Change *to* to *too*
   D Make no change

   S.3

2. What change, if any, should be made in sentence 9?
   A Change the period after *planets* to an exclamation mark
   B Change *Their* to *There*
   C Change *are* to *our*
   D Make no change

   S.9

3. What change, if any, should be made in sentence 10?
   A Change *one* to *won*
   B Add a comma after *travels*
   C Change *around* to *a round*
   D Make no change

   S.10

4. Which of the following is **NOT** a complete sentence?
   A Sentence 2
   B Sentence 9
   C Sentence 15
   D Sentence 16

5. What change, if any, should be made in sentence 17?
   A Change *Four* to *For*
   B Change *goes* to *gos*
   C Change *around* to *a round*
   D Make no change

   S.17

6. Which sentence could **BEST** be added after sentence 18?
   A Earth is the third planet from the Sun.
   B It takes 687 days for Mars to orbit the Sun.
   C At one time, the planet Venus had water.
   D Meteors and comets streak across the horizon.

Name_____ Date_____

7 What change, if any, should be made to sentence 19?

A   Change the period after *planets* to an exclamation mark

B   Change *Sun* to *sun*

C   Change *nearer* to *nearest*

D   Make no change

8 What is the **BEST** way to combine the ideas in sentences 21 and 22?

A   The inner planets are small and made of solid rock.

B   The small planets are made of solid rock.

C   Inside the planets are small, solid rocks.

D   The inner planets are small and the inner planets are made of solid rock.

9 What change, if any, should be made in sentence 27?

A   Add a comma after *Jupiter*

B   Change *read* to *red*

C   Add a comma after *are*

D   Make no change

10 Which sentence could **BEST** be added after sentence 28?

A   The outer planets are quite cold.

B   The outer planets are the best planets.

C   Earth is an inner planet.

D   The planet Mars has two moons.

Name_____ **Date**_____

WRITE

Write about an astronaut's journey into space.

The box below will help you write your composition. Then write your composition on another piece of paper.

REMEMBER TO—

☐ write about an astronaut's journey into space

☐ include details about where the astronaut goes and what the astronaut sees there

☐ include vivid language so your reader can imagine what the astronaut sees on the space journey

☐ check for correct spelling, capitalization, punctuation, grammar, and sentences ·········

Look back for commonly misused words such as there, their, and they're.

Name_____ Date_____

REVIEW

Compare and Contrast

When you **compare** two things, you tell how they are alike. When you **contrast** two things, you tell how they are different. To answer a compare-and-contrast question, ask yourself:

• How are the two things mentioned in the question *alike*?

• How are the two things mentioned in the question *different*?

Sometimes you will be asked to compare or contrast ideas or information within a single selection. At other times, you will be asked to compare or contrast across two selections.

Read the passage. Then answer the questions that follow.

No Longer a Pup

The playful young wolf was just one year old. He was no longer a pup, but he wasn't a full-grown adult yet either. Like people, wolves pass through a middle stage as they grow from baby to adult. In human terms, the wolf would be considered a teenager or young adult.

1 What two things are being compared?

   To human.

2 How are the two things alike?

   A teenager or young adult

3 How are they different?

   _____

When you are asked to compare and contrast, go back to the passages and underline words about the things you are asked to compare and contrast.

Name Emilio ~~A milia~~ **Date** 12-11-04

PRACTICE

Compare and Contrast

Read the two selections. Then read each question that follows the selections. Decide which is the best answer to each question. Mark the letter for that answer.

Dr. Carl Haberlein lived in Germany in the middle 1800s. He was an amateur collector of fossils. The fictional letter below tells about an interesting experience he had. A museum pamphlet about archaeopteryx follows the letter.

From Dr. Carl Haberlein

Fall, 1863

Dearest Brother,

1   An extraordinary thing has happened. As you know, many of my patients are far from wealthy and are sometimes unable to compensate me for my services. I have always agreed to accept goods or favors as payment.

2   Recently I treated a fellow from the university who had hurt his leg while on an archeological dig in Solnhofen. Like many students, he had little money. Still, he was quite thankful for the medical attention and wanted to show his gratitude. Now, you know how much I enjoy collecting old bones and stones. I told him that I would be happy to accept as payment a specimen from the site where he was digging. The fellow gladly agreed.

3   The next day he presented me with a collection of bones such that I had never seen. I called on my friend H. von Meyer, who knows a great deal about these matters. He was impressed with the bones and stated that this was a most unique find. It seems I had in my possession the remains of an ancient bird, possibly the first one ever to take to the skies!

4   H. von Meyer contacted Richard Owen at the British Museum about permanently housing this fossil in London. I am looking forward to Mr. Owen's reply and will let you know soon what the British Museum has decided.

Until then, I remain

Your brother, Carl

Name Emilio   **Date**

Museum of Dinosaurs

Information for Young Scientists (Pamphlet 1)

Archaeopteryx

1   The earliest known bird lived at the time of the dinosaurs. That was about 140 million years ago. Scientists call this early bird *archaeopteryx* (ahr-kee-OP-tuhr-iks). Its name means "ancient wing." In some ways it was like modern birds, but it was also very different.

2   *Archaeopteryx* looked like a mix of different animals. Because of the feathers on its body, it looked like a bird. However, it also had a long pointed nose and sharp teeth. These features made it look like a small dinosaur. Unlike today's birds, which have no teeth, the *archaeopteryx* could not only peck, it could bite! Its strong hind legs and sharp claws also made it look partly like a lizard. It even had three little "fingers" with sharp claws at the end of each wing. *Archaeopteryx* was truly a strange animal. No wonder scientists were so surprised when they first discovered it!

3   Today, some scientists think that even though *archaeopteryx* had feathers, its wings were weak. It probably could not really fly like a bird. Instead, it probably used its claws to climb the trunks of trees. Then it spread its wings and glided through the air. It probably flew much like today's flying squirrel. A flying squirrel uses flaps of skin stretched between its legs to glide, just as *archaeopteryx* might have used its wings.

#8
#7

Name Emilio   Date

1   Dr. Haberlein's letter was
    mainly written to—

    A   share information about an
        unusual event

    B   teach a lesson about
        archaeology

    C   describe the features of an
        ancient bird

    D   persuade the reader to visit
        a museum

2   In paragraph 1 of the letter, the
    word compensate means—

    A   to restore balance

    B   to understand

    C   to warn against

    D   to make payment to

    P.1

3   In paragraph 4 of the letter, the
    word housing means—

    A   a place of residence

    B   a legislative body

    C   providing with a house

    D   storing safely in a building

    P.4

4   What is the most likely way
    that Mr. Owen replied?

    A   By E-mail

    B   By letter

    C   By telephone

    D   By satellite

5   Which statement is true of both
    archaeopteryx and a flying
    squirrel?

    A   They have clawlike "fingers"
        at the end of each wing.

    B   They have flaps of skin
        between their legs.

    C   They have weak wings.

    D   They can glide through
        the air.

6   How was archaeopteryx
    different from today's birds?

    A   Archaeopteryx had stronger
        wings than today's birds do.

    B   Archaeopteryx had teeth,
        but today's birds do not.

    C   Archaeopteryx had claws,
        but today's birds do not.

    D   Archaeopteryx had feathers,
        but today's birds do not.

    P.2

Name _Emilio_   Date _____

7 In paragraph 3 of the pamphlet, the word trunks means—

  A the main stems of plants apart from limbs and roots

  B boxes used to store items

  C the soil in which a tree is grown

  D a plant's leaves or branches

        P.3

8 Look at this outline of information from the pamphlet.

> **I.** What did *archaeopteryx* look like?
>
>   **A.** Had feathers like a bird
>
>   **B.** _____
>
>   **C.** Had strong hind legs and sharp claws like a lizard
>
>   **D.** Had three little "fingers" with sharp claws at the end of each wing

Which information belongs in the blank?

  A Had weak wings

  B Had a long pointed nose and sharp teeth

  C Could peck and bite

  D Was truly a strange animal

P3

9 How is the information presented in the letter?

  A The earliest events are mentioned first, followed by later events.

  B The main problem is stated first. Then several solutions are listed.

  C A cause is stated first. Then several effects are listed.

  D An opinion is stated first, followed by facts supporting that opinion.

10 Unlike Dr. Haberlein, the author of the pamphlet knows—

  A fossils are important

  B fossils were found at an archaeological dig

  C the ancient birdlike creature was called *archaeopteryx*

  D the fossils would be stored at the British Museum

© Macmillan/McGraw-Hill

Name_____ Date_____

REVIEW

Prepositional Phrases

A **prepositional phrase** is made up of a **preposition**, the **object of the preposition**, and all the words in between.

- A **preposition** often tells where an object is, what an object is like, or where it is from. Examples: in, by, near, above, from, to

- The **object of the preposition** is the noun or pronoun that follows the preposition. Examples: on the <u>fence</u>, with <u>her</u>, below the <u>tree</u>, by the <u>sidewalk</u>

You can use prepositional phrases to make your writing more descriptive and to help link ideas.

Using a preposition from the box, rewrite each sentence, adding a prepositional phrase to make it more descriptive.

in   beside   behind   on   above

Example: Put the glass on the shelf.

<u>Put the glass on the shelf above the stove.</u>

1   I left my coat at home.

   I left my coat at home beside the coach.

2   The deer eat the grass.

   The deer eat the grass above the earth.

3   I played at the park.

   I played at the park in the summer.

Use prepositional phrases to add vivid details to your writing.

Name_____ Date_____

PRACTICE

Prepositional Phrases

A fourth grader at Lago Vista Elementary School, Daniel, is writing a story about a boy who wants to play on the school basketball team. Read Daniel's story and think about improvements he could make. Then answer the questions that follow.

The New Team Member

(1) Marcus's new school had a basketball team, and Marcus wanted to be on the team. (2) On the first day of school, a friendly boy approached Marcus. (3) "Hey, you're Marcus, right? (4) My name's LeRoy," the tall, thin boy said as he came over to the table. (5) "I heard you like to play basketball."

(6) Before Marcus could answer, LeRoy said, "Well, I'm on the team. (7) How about shooting some baskets with us? (8) We'll be in the gym after school."

(9) All day, Marcus kept looking at his watch. (10) When the school day was finally over, Marcus runned to the gym. (11) He had just entered, when the coach walked over to him. (12) "LeRoy was telling me about you," the coach said. (13) "How about trying a few shots?"

(14) Marcus took the ball from the coach. (15) He bounced it a few times. (16) He didn't want to make a careless shot. (17) He took a deep breath to calm his nerves. (18) Then he aimed carefully at the basket. (19) The ball dropped through the hoop perfectly. (20) The coach tossed

Name_____ Date_____

him the ball again. (21) Marcus took four more shots. (22) They all went in. (23) Every one went through the hoop cleanly.

(24) "Listen," the coach said. (25) "If you would like to play on the team, we're meeting tomorrow afternoon for two hours. (26) It's the teams first practice session." (27) If Marcus hadn't heard it, he wouldn't have believed it. (28) He was going to be on the team. (29) He felt like the happiest boy there!

1 How could sentence 2 **BEST** be rewritten to include a prepositional phrase?

A On the first day of school, a friendly boy approached Marcus and said hello.

B On the first day of school, a friendly boy approached Marcus in the lunchroom.

C On the first day of school, a friendly boy approached Marcus, and Marcus was at lunch.

D On the very first day of school, a friendly boy approached Marcus.

2 Which is the **BEST** way to combine sentences 7 and 8?

A "How about shooting some baskets with us, and we'll be in the gym after school."

B "How about shooting some baskets with us, we're in the gym after school?"

C "How about shooting some baskets? With us in the gym after school."

D "How about shooting some baskets with us in the gym after school?"

Name_____ **Date**_____

3 What change, if any, should be made in sentence 10?

   A Change *school* to **School**

   B Change *was* to **were**

   C Change *runned* to **ran**

   D Make no change

4 Which prepositional phrase could **BEST** be added at the end of sentence 13?

   A from the free throw line

   B by today

   C with the player

   D in the gym

5 Which is the **BEST** way to combine sentences 14 and 15?

   A Marcus took the ball from the coach, he bounced it a few times.

   B Marcus took the ball from the coach and bounced it a few times.

   C Marcus took the ball from the coach, he was bouncing it a few times.

   D Marcus took the ball from the coach, bounced it a few times.

6 Which is the **BEST** way to combine sentences 21 and 22?

   A Marcus took four more shots, and they all went in.

   B Marcus took four more shots, but they all went in.

   C Marcus took four more shots, all went in.

   D Marcus took four more shots, they all went in.

7 What change, if any, should be made in sentence 25?

   A Change *like* to **liking**

   B Change *we're* to **were**

   C Change *tomorrow* to **tomorow**

   D Make no change

8 What change, if any, should be made in sentence 26?

   A Change *It's* to **Its**

   B Change *teams* to **team's**

   C Add a comma after *first*

   D Make no change

© Macmillan/McGraw-Hill

Name_____ Date_____

9 How could sentence 27 **BEST** be rewritten to include a prepositional phrase?

A If Marcus hadn't heard it, he wouldn't have believed it at first.

B If Marcus hadn't heard it with his own ears, he wouldn't have believed it.

C If Marcus hadn't heard the coach, he wouldn't have believed the news.

D If Marcus hadn't heard it, he wouldn't have believed it from the coach.

10 The meaning of sentence 29 can be improved by changing *there* to—

A in the lunchroom

B in the whole school

C of the day

D their

Name_____ Date_____

WRITE

> Write about a trip you'd like to go on with your class.

The box below will help you write your composition. Then write your composition on another piece of paper.

REMEMBER TO—

- ❏ describe a class trip you would like to take

- ❏ make sure to include details about where you would like to go and what you would do and see

- ❏ use descriptive language so your reader can imagine the place you would like to see ......

- ❏ check for correct capitalization, spelling, punctuation, and grammar

> *Can you add any prepositional phrases to make the sentences more descriptive?*

Name *Emilio Cáceres* 1-28-10 **Date** 1-28-10

REVIEW

Author's Bias: Fact and Opinion and Point of View

Many passages contain a combination of **facts** and **opinions**. A **fact** is a piece of information that can be proven. An **opinion** is a statement of what someone thinks or feels about something.

To determine whether a statement is a fact or an opinion, ask:

• Can the statement be proven, or is it a well-known fact?

• Does the statement give someone's views or feelings?

The way an author feels about a subject affects the way he or she writes about it. This is called the author's **point of view**. To answer a question about an author's point of view, ask:

• What clues in the text show how the author feels about this?

Read each sentence below. Then answer the questions that follow.

1   The bluebonnet is the most beautiful flower.
    Is this a fact or opinion? How do you know?

    opinion Because is the most beutiful

2   The bluebonnet is the state flower of Texas.
    Is this a fact or opinion? How do you know?

    Fact. Because in can be proven

3   "Wildflowers must be protected by the state!"
    —Loren Larsen, director of the Texas Wildflower Research Center
    What is Mr. Larsen's point of view?

    protect the flowers.

Name Emilio Caceres   **Date** 1-28-10

~2

80

TAKS PRACTICE

Author's Bias: Fact and Opinion and Point of View

Read the selection. Then read each question that follows the selection. Decide which is the best answer to each question. Mark the letter for that answer.

And Another Thing . . .

24 Oakwood St.

Longview, TX 75601

May 19, 2002

Dear Mayor Sledge:

1   I am writing to share some information that you really need to know. Today I was sitting in the park, watching my granddaughter play. All of a sudden, a large dog came running past me, and the dog was not on a leash! It knocked a boy down. That poor little boy will be afraid of dogs for the rest of his life, and all because of some irresponsible dog owner. Then there was another dog, again without a leash, chasing a squirrel. The precious squirrel looked so defenseless against that mean dog. The poor baby barely made it up the tree in time.

2   In the evenings dog owners form some sort of club. They let their dogs run together in a pack without leashes. They say the dogs are playing, but it sure doesn't feel like play when you're minding your own business jogging down the path and these beasts all come

Name Emilio Caceres   **Date** 4-28-10

chasing after you. I have as much right to use the park as the dog owners, but I feel afraid to go jogging in a park that my taxes help to maintain.

3   Just last week, when I was sitting on my front porch enjoying the beautiful night, a car full of teenagers parked across from my house with their radio blaring. The loud rock music was unbearable. I could barely hear myself think! And then the next day, a boy and girl sat down on a blanket near the park bench where I was sitting. They had a large boom box turned up so loud I thought my eardrums would shatter! Not only did the music bother me, but the vibrations from the speakers set off a car alarm in a truck parked ten yards away. Something must be done about the noise!

4   And yesterday, when I was going to the post office, I was almost run over by a young man on a skateboard. I stepped onto the sidewalk, and he nearly took my arm off as he rolled past! Then, after I came out of the post office, another hooligan on a skateboard barreled past me and almost knocked me senseless. Skateboards are such a hazard!

5   I thought I should pass along this information, Mr. Mayor, because this town just isn't safe anymore—not with these attack dogs, these lightning fast skateboards, and all the eardrum-blasting noise pollution. I ask you, Mr. Mayor, aren't there any regulations about these things? Shouldn't dogs be on leashes at all times? Perhaps people who let their dogs run wild should be fined. And how do I go about getting my street turned into a quiet zone like the blocks around the hospital? Can we not insist that people playing music outside wear headphones? Also, there should be a law requiring young people to have to go to safety classes and receive licenses before they are allowed to ride skateboards. Drivers are ticketed when they break traffic laws. Shouldn't skateboarders be ticketed as well? Every day it just gets worse! It's up to you to do something. I'm hopeful that you will—if you'd like to get re-elected next fall!

Sincerely,

Mrs. Rita Worth

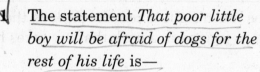

Name Emilio Caceres   **Date** 1-28-10

1 The statement *That poor little boy will be afraid of dogs for the rest of his life* is—

A an opinion because nobody knows how the boy will feel ?

B an opinion because being knocked down is scary ✗

P.1 **C** a fact because the boy looked very frightened ✗

D a fact because it can be proven that the dog knocked the boy down ✗

2 Which sentence is an opinion?

A *I was sitting in the park.* ✗

B *It knocked a boy down.* ✗

C *There was another dog, again without a leash.* ✗

P.1 **D** *The precious squirrel looked so defenseless against that mean dog.* ?

3 How does Mrs. Worth probably feel about dogs?

A She is allergic to dogs. ✗

B She doesn't like dogs. ✗

C She thinks dogs make good pets. ?

D She wants a dog herself. ✗

4 Why did Mrs. Worth tell the mayor about the dog incidents?

A She wants the mayor to make a cat the town mascot. ✗

B She thinks dogs should be kept on leashes. ?

C It was the mayor's dog that knocked the boy down. ✗

D Her granddaughter wants a puppy. ✗

5 Which sentence is a fact?

A *A car full of teenagers parked across from my house.* ?

B *The loud rock music was unbearable.* ✗

C *I thought my eardrums would shatter!* ✗

D *Something must be done!* ✗

6 Why did Mrs. Worth tell the mayor about the loud music?

A She thinks skateboards are dangerous. ✗

B She thinks the mayor listens to loud music. ✗

P.3 **C** She thinks loud music should be banned outdoors. ?

D She wants to recommend some CDs. ✗

© Macmillan/McGraw-Hill

Name Emilio Caceres   **Date** 1-28-10

7 Which sentence is an opinion?

A *I was going to the post office.*

B *Drivers are ticketed when they break traffic laws.*

C *I stepped onto the sidewalk.*

D *Skateboards are such a hazard!*

8 Why did Mrs. Worth tell the mayor about the skateboard incidents?

A To describe how dangerous young people are

B To persuade the mayor to license skateboarders

C To convince the mayor to move the post office

D To explain how to ride a skateboard safely

9 What is the most likely reason Mrs. Worth wrote this letter?

A She wants the mayor to take action against dogs, loud music, and skateboards.

B She wants to be appointed to the city council.

C She wants to sell the mayor a boom box.

D She is an old friend of the mayor.

10 In paragraph 5, the word hopeful means—

A full of hope

B without hope

C after hope

D hope again

Name_____ Date_____

REVIEW

Writing Complete Sentences

A **sentence fragment** is missing either a subject or a predicate.

The *subject* tells who or what the sentence is about. The *predicate* tells what the subject did or what the subject is like.

Fragment: My white cat, Tinkerbell.

Correct: My white cat, Tinkerbell, likes to sit in the sun.

A **run-on sentence** is two or more sentences written as one. Run-on sentences can be corrected by separating sentences or by combining them using conjunctions such as *and*, *or*, and *but*.

Run-On: My mom drove to the store she bought some fruit.

Correct: My mom drove to the store. She bought some fruit.
　　　　 My mom drove to the store and bought some fruit.

To the left of each sentence, write *C* for complete sentence, *F* for fragment, or *R* for run-on. Then write the sentence correctly. If the sentence is complete, write *Make no change*.

F **1** The bright stars in the night sky.

The bright stars in the night of the sky

C **2** Maria loves to swim she has won many races.

Make no change

C **3** I will practice for the concert on Saturday morning.

Make no change

F **4** The cucumber seedlings.

The cucumber seedling are delicious

Name_____ Date_____

PRACTICE

Writing Complete Sentences

Donna is writing an article for the Hill Elementary School newspaper about a fourth-grade class that helped protect a beach. Read her article and consider the improvements she might make. Then answer the multiple-choice questions that follow.

Students Save the Dunes

(1) The fourth-grade boy tugged at the used Christmas tree. (2) The tree was taller than the boy, he pulled until the tree was standing alongside the others. (3) It must have been a peculiar sight. (4) Members of a fourth-grade class were "planting" used Christmas trees. (5) In sand dunes on their town's beach.

(6) Sand dunes are hills of sand. (7) They protect coastal areas. (8) From rising ocean water and blowing winds. (9) They also provide a home for certain plants and animals. (10) Years of crashing waves and blowing winds had destroyed many of the sand dunes near Margate, New Jersey. (11) Volunteers had tried to solve the problem they placed trees sideways on the sand, hoping to hold the dunes in place. (12) Sadly, the plan did not work. (13) The trees washed out to see. (14) In storms and high tides.

(15) Then students in a fourth-grade class at Union Avenue School came up with a new idea. (16) They decided to place the trees, standing up, along the beach. (17) They hoped the tree limbs would catch the

Name_____ **Date**_____

blowing sand. (18) If that happened, then new dunes wood form around the trees.

(19) The first thing these students did was dig a trench, or small ditch, in the sand. (20) Then they stood the trees in the trench. (21) Finally, they filled sand in around the tree trunks this held the trees firmly in place. (22) To make sure their plan was working. (23) Students tied red ribbons to the treetops. (24) Week by week, they measured the distance from each ribbon to the sand. (25) Sure enough, the students discovered that the level of sand was rising. (26) Their project was a success!

1 Which is the **BEST** way to rewrite the ideas in sentence 2?

   A The tree was taller than the boy, but he pulled until the tree was standing alongside the others.

   B The tree was taller. Then the boy pulled until the tree was standing alongside the others.

   C The tree was taller than the boy. He pulled. The tree was standing alongside the others.

   D The tree was taller than the boy, or he pulled until the tree was standing alongside the others.

2 Which of the following is **NOT** a complete sentence?

   A Sentence 1

   B Sentence 3

   C Sentence 4

   D Sentence 5

3 Which of the following is **NOT** a complete sentence?

   A Sentence 6

   B Sentence 7

   C Sentence 8

   D Sentence 9

Name_____ Date_____

4 What change, if any, should be made in sentence 10?

A   Change *destroyed* to **destroied**

B   Change *dunes* to **dune's**

C   Add a comma after *winds* and another comma after *destroyed*

D   Make no change

5 Which is the **BEST** way to rewrite the ideas in sentence 11?

A   Volunteers had tried to solve the problem, they placed trees sideways on the sand, hoping to hold the dunes in place.

B   Volunteers had tried to solve the problem. They placed trees sideways on the sand, hoping to hold the dunes in place.

C   Volunteers had tried. To solve the problem, they placed trees sideways on the sand. The trees hold the dunes in place.

D   Volunteers had tried to solve the problem, but they placed trees sideways on the sand, hoping to hold the dunes in place.

6 What change, if any, should be made in sentence 13?

A   Change *see* to **sea**

B   Change *washed* to **wash**

C   Change *to* to **too**

D   Make no change

7 Which of the following is **NOT** a complete sentence?

A   Sentence 13

B   Sentence 14

C   Sentence 15

D   Sentence 16

8 What change, if any, should be made in sentence 18?

A   Change *that* to **that's**

B   Change *wood* to **would**

C   Change *form* to **forms**

D   Make no change

Name_____ Date_____

9 Which is the **BEST** way to rewrite the ideas in sentence 21?

A Finally, they filled sand in around the tree trunks, this held the trees firmly in place.

B Finally, they filled sand in around the tree trunks. This held the trees firmly in place.

C Finally, they filled sand in around the tree trunks, but this held the trees firmly in place.

D Finally, they filled sand in. Around the tree trunks this held the trees firmly in place.

10 Which of the following is **NOT** a complete sentence?

A Sentence 22

B Sentence 23

C Sentence 25

D Sentence 26

Name_____ **Date**_____

WRITE

> Write about a class project that would benefit your community.

The box below will help you write your composition. Then write your composition on another piece of paper.

REMEMBER TO—

☐ describe a project that would benefit your community

☐ make sure to include details that explain what you would like to do and what benefits it would have

☐ use descriptive language so your reader can imagine the project you are writing about

☐ make sure to use correct spelling, capitalization, punctuation, grammar, and complete sentences

Check for sentence fragments.

Student Name _____

TAKS
Texas Assessment of Knowledge and Skills
Grade 4 Reading Practice Test

DIRECTIONS

Read each selection. Then read each question that follows the
selection. Decide which is the best answer to each question. Fill
in the circle on your Answer Sheet.

Abigail Adams

#1

1   Abigail Adams was born in 1744 in Weymouth, Massachusetts. At that time, Massachusetts was an English colony. Her father, William Smith, was a minister who came from a wealthy family. Her mother, Elizabeth Quincy Smith, also came from a wealthy family. Abigail was often sick as a child. She was not able to go to school. Even though she couldn't go to school, Abigail was eager to learn. Her parents wanted her to become educated as well. Her father had a large private library. He wanted his children to learn to read.

2   Abigail loved books and used them to teach herself about many topics. She loved reading history, poetry, and drama. Abigail said that learning was like "visiting a beautiful country." Because of her love of reading, Abigail became one of the most knowledgeable women of her time.

3   At the age of 19, Abigail married John Adams, a young lawyer. At first they lived outside of Boston. Soon they moved into the city. Abigail and John had five children—Abigail, John Quincy, Susanna, Charles, and Thomas.

#2

4   While living in Boston, Abigail read books and newspapers. She made friends with other families. Her husband was often away on business. Abigail stayed home to raise their children.

5   John and Abigail wanted the American colonies to become free from England. When the colonies declared their independence in 1776, John moved to Philadelphia. He helped set up the new nation. Abigail stayed home with the children. She learned what was happening from newspapers and John's letters. During the Revolutionary War (1775–1783), Abigail wrote hundreds of letters to her husband. Her letters record ideas and events from this important time in our country's history.

6   In her letters, Abigail told John what she thought. She had many ideas. She wanted better education for women. "Remember the ladies," she reminded her husband as he wrote new laws, "and be more generous and favorable to them than your ancestors." Abigail's letters also provided her husband with valuable information about British troops and ships in the Boston area.

© Macmillan/McGraw-Hill

7   In 1782, John Adams moved to Europe to represent our new nation in meetings with French and British government officials. Abigail remained at home. She wanted to make sure her children were educated at school.

8   In 1789, John became Vice President of the United States. Again, he left his home in Massachusetts. He moved to Philadelphia, the nation's capital at that time. Soon after he arrived he wrote to Abigail, "I must have you here to assist me." She joined him a short time later.

9   John Adams became the country's second President in 1797. He thought of his wife as a partner in his work and often asked her what she thought. He valued Abigail's judgment and insights. In 1800 the couple moved into the new White House in Washington, D.C. They became the first family to live in the White House. The building was still unfinished. When they moved in, only about six rooms in the White House were completed. The remaining rooms were still under construction.

10   John's term as President ended in 1801. He and Abigail went home to Massachusetts. Later their son, John Quincy Adams, also became President. That made Abigail Adams the wife of one President and the mother of another.

11   No other woman could make that claim until 2001, when George W. Bush was sworn in as President. His mother, Barbara Bush, was the wife of President George H. Bush. Mrs. Bush was proud to share a distinctive place in our nation's history with the remarkable Mrs. Adams.

1 Paragraph 1 is mostly about—

   A Abigail Adams's childhood

   B Abigail Adams's children

   C Abigail Adams's father

   D Abigail Adams's birthplace

2 In paragraph 4, the word <u>raise</u> means—

   A to bring up and help grow

   B to lift up

   C to increase in pay

   D to increase in value

3 What did Abigail mean when she compared learning to "visiting a beautiful country"?

   A Only by traveling can you really learn new things.

   B Learning gives you a way to enjoy new experiences.

   C The best way to learn is by reading about other places.

   D Natural beauty is better than books.

4 This article suggests that John Adams—

   A did not value women

   B preferred life at home

   C respected his wife's ideas

   D liked being a lawyer

5 Which of the following best summarizes the article?

   A John Adams went to Philadelphia to help organize the new nation. Abigail Adams stayed home. She wrote letters.

   B Abigail Adams was well educated and liked to write letters. She was lonely when her husband was away. They had five children.

   C Abigail Adams was born in 1744. She was very well read and knowledgeable. Abigail's advice was valued by her husband John, who was a leader during the Revolutionary War and later became President.

   D Abigail's letters to her husband helped America during the Revolutionary War. They also provide important historical information today.

6 This article was written mainly to—

   A persuade the reader to support women's rights

   B entertain the reader with stories about colonial life

   C inform the reader about the life of Abigail Adams

   D inform the reader about the American Revolution

7 According to the article, Abigail Adams became one of the most knowledgeable women of her time because—

A she read many books on various topics

B her father made her read every day

C she was an outstanding student in college

D her husband kept her informed on important issues

8 From what the reader learns about Abigail Adams, which statement would not be reasonable?

A Abigail Adams thought that women didn't need formal schooling.

B Abigail Adams thought that women needed more educational opportunities.

C Abigail Adams thought that taking care of her children was important.

D Abigail Adams thought that America should be free from England.

9 What can the reader tell about Abigail Adams from reading this article?

A Abigail Adams was not interested in politics.

B Abigail Adams had strong ideas about women's rights.

C Abigail Adams did not enjoy school.

D Abigail Adams did not think formal schooling was important.

10 Look at the diagram.

John Adams	Both	Abigail Adams
• Lawyer • Statesman • Vice President • President	• _____	• Minister's Daughter • Women's Rights Advocate • Mother • First Lady

Which of the following goes in the blank?

A Valued education

B Lived overseas

C Raised in Philadelphia

D Came from poor families

Read the next two selections. Then answer the questions that follow them.

100%

A Letter from Jamal

Dear Grandma and Grandpa,

1   How are you? I sure had fun visiting you last month. Playing in your pecan orchard is so much fun! I really enjoyed helping you gather the pecans. My mom is still baking cookies with the pecans I brought back with me.

2   I know you've talked to Mom and Dad about buying a pet for Tamara and me. That's really nice of you! I hope you will get us a dog. I think dogs make the best pets. Let me tell you why I think so.

3   First, dogs are very smart. You can teach them lots of tricks. You can teach dogs to sit, fetch a ball, and roll over. You can teach them to play dead and to speak. You can also teach a dog to walk on a leash. I would really like to have a dog that I can take with me to the park and on walks around the neighborhood. I know we would have lots of fun together!

4   Second, dogs are very loyal. They will greet you when you come home. They will bark to let you know when someone is near your house. It's like having your own burglar alarm! They have shown that they can sense danger and can protect you from harm. Dogs love to curl up at your feet. They can keep you company when you are alone.

5   Finally, dogs are really cute! Their soft fur and wagging tails always make me smile. Their big, brown eyes always make my heart feel good, too.

6   I hope you get us a dog. I promise to take good care of it!

Love,
Jamal

A Letter from Tamara

Dear Grandma and Grandpa,

1   How are you? I hope you're both feeling well. I just found out some great news. I made the school volleyball team. I hope you can come to my first game!

2   Mom tells me that you want to get us a pet. That would be great! I hope you will get us a cat. Cats make the best pets. Here's why I think so.

3   First, cats are very smart. They always know how to get what they want. If they want you to pet them, they hop in your lap. If cats want to be left alone, they hide and can be really hard to find. They also tell you when they want to be fed. They meow and rub themselves against your leg until you agree to feed them.

4   Second, cats are very dainty. They eat their food slowly and neatly, and they usually eat just a little at a time. They don't wolf their food down like dogs do. They also love to keep themselves clean. They are always licking their paws and their fur so they can be neat and pretty. And they never knock you down like dogs do. They jump lightly into your lap, or they sit quietly beside you.

5   Finally, cats are beautiful. They are graceful and delicate, and their fur is always soft and clean. Their whiskers tickle, too, when they give you kisses.

6   I hope you get us a cat. I'll take good care of it!

Love,
Tamara

11 Which sentence from Jamal's letter explains why he compares a dog to a burglar alarm?

A *First, dogs are very smart.*

B *Second, dogs are very loyal.*

C *Dogs love to curl up at your feet.*

D *They will bark to let you know when someone is near your house.*

P.4

12 Paragraph 4 is mostly about—

A how dogs look

B what dogs eat

C how dogs make good companions

D how dogs can learn many tricks

P.4

13 Read this outline of information from Jamal's letter.

> **A.** Dogs are loyal
>   **1.** Greet you when you come home
>   **2.** Bark at strangers
>   **3.** _____
>   **4.** Keep you company

Which information belongs in the blank?

A Have big, brown eyes

B When someone is in your yard

C Can protect you from harm

D Can teach dogs tricks

P.4

14 The most likely reason Jamal wrote this letter to his grandparents was to—

A thank them for the pecans

B entertain them with stories about dogs

C inform them about the habits of dogs

D persuade them to buy him a dog

15 Which of the following statements from Tamara's letter is a fact in the selection?

(A) *I made the school volleyball team.*

B *Cats make the best pets.*

C *Second, cats are very dainty.*

D *Finally, cats are beautiful.*

16 Paragraph 4 is mostly about—

A how cats are prettier than dogs

(B) how cats behave better than dogs

C how cats are more intelligent than dogs

D how cats and dogs make good pets

P.4

17 Look at this web with information about cats from Tamara's letter.

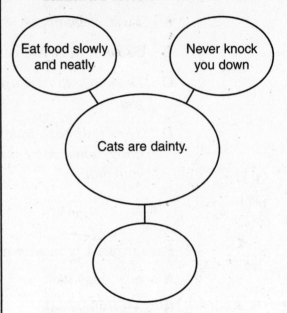

Which of these belongs in the empty circle?

(A) Keep themselves clean

B Meow when strangers come near

C Always wolf down their food

D Sit when you tell them to

P.5

18 According to the letters, how are cats and dogs alike?

   A Both are neat eaters.

   B Both are smart.

   C Both like to do tricks.

   D Both are good protectors.

P.3
both stories

19 How are Tamara and Jamal related to each other?

   A They are best friends.

   B They are sister and brother.

   C They are neighbors.

   D They are not related.

20 Look at this diagram comparing the two letters.

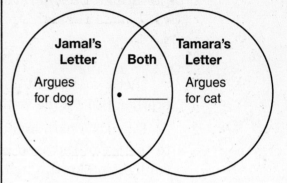

Which of these best completes the diagram?

   A Agree on which animal makes best pet

   B Are written by same person

   C Present information for the same purpose

   D Tell interesting stories about the writers

The question of why whales sometimes wash up on beaches has long fascinated scientists around the world. Sometimes whales beach themselves because they are sick or they have been injured by boat propellers. Some stranded whales are babies that somehow became separated from their mothers. In this fictional story, Nina and her brother spot a beached whale during their walk along the seashore.

Save the Whale! 100%

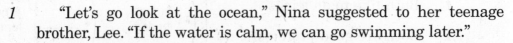

1   "Let's go look at the ocean," Nina suggested to her teenage brother, Lee. "If the water is calm, we can go swimming later."

2   Down the path and through the dune grass they went, then up to the top of the sand hill overlooking the beach. As they walked, sunlight broke through the clouds and the sky brightened. Nina hummed and skipped excitedly as she climbed up the dunes.

#21

3   "The ocean is so calm!" cried Nina. "We're going to have a great beach day!"

#22

4   "We sure are," agreed her brother, "but what's that?" He was pointing to a large dark shape at the edge of the water.

5   "I can't tell," answered his sister, straining her eyes to see.

6   "Maybe it's a shark," guessed her brother.

7   "No," Nina said, "it's a whale! It looks just like the one I saw on television a few weeks ago."

8   "Do you know what's the matter with it?" asked Lee. "Do you think it swam up here by mistake?"

9   "I don't think so," his sister replied. "Maybe the storm washed it ashore. Sometimes whales beach themselves for reasons no one really understands. They swim into shallow water and get stuck on the sand. When the tide goes out, they are left high and dry."

10   Nina and Lee walked towards the whale to get a closer look. It didn't take them long to realize that the animal was in trouble.

11   By the time they raced back to the house, their grandfather was up and preparing breakfast. Nina told him most of the story, and Lee supplied the missing details.

12   When they were finished, Grandpa said, "I'll call the county Wildlife Department. They have officers who can help."

13   Twenty minutes later, Nina, Lee, and their grandfather all went down to the beach to wait. The whale now lay in shallow water. A few minutes later, Dr. Kaplow, a vet from the Wildlife Department, was checking the whale. A group of experts from the Wildlife Department stood nearby and watched.

14   "Can we help?" asked Nina.

15   "You already did just by calling us," replied Dr. Kaplow. "I've given the whale a check-up, and it seems unharmed."

16   "Why are they pouring buckets of seawater over the whale?" asked Lee.

17   "In the sun and warm air, a whale's body temperature will rise," Dr. Kaplow explained. "That can be very dangerous for the whale. Drenching it in seawater will help cool it down."

18   "Is that why they are putting wet blankets over the whale?" asked Nina.

19   "They also want to make sure the whale doesn't get a sunburn," Dr. Kaplow continued. "See how they are making sure not to cover the whale's blowhole? If they did, the whale couldn't breathe."

20   All morning the Wildlife Department officers continued keeping the whale cool and wet. Finally, the tide rose and the officers pushed the whale out into deeper water. Slowly it swam away. Nina's eyes sparkled as she continued to watch the whale disappear into the ocean.

21   "I'm glad it's okay," said Nina.

22   "That's one lucky whale," said Dr. Kaplow, "and he has you and your brother to thank for it."

21 Which sentence from the story shows the reader where the story takes place?

   A *It didn't take them long to realize that the animal was in trouble.*

   B *Down the path and through the dune grass they went, then up to the top of the sand hill overlooking the beach.*

   C *When they were finished, Grandpa said, "I'll call the county Wildlife Department."*

   D *In the sun and warm air, a whale's body temperature will rise.*

P.2

22 How did Nina feel when she and Lee went to the beach that morning?

   A Nervous because of the storm

   B Excited about going to the beach

   C Worried about what they might find after the storm

   D Tired because she didn't get enough sleep the night before

P.3

23 The author organizes the story by—

   A telling events in the order in which they occurred

   B providing facts about stranded whales

   C comparing two very different kinds of whales

   D including helpful facts in the margins around the fictional story

24 In paragraph 15, the word unharmed means—

   A injured

   B frightened

   C dangerous

   D not hurt   P.15

25 What problem did Nina and Lee face?

   A They wanted to save a whale.

   B They needed their grandfather's help.

   C They were afraid the whale would injure them.

   D They needed to help feed the stranded whale.

© Macmillan/McGraw-Hill

26 How did Nina and Lee solve their problem?

A They used water to keep the whale cool.

B They waited until high tide to push the whale out to sea.

C They got their grandfather to help them find people to help the whale.

D They went to Ocean World to get a veterinarian.

27 Read the chart below. It shows the order in which some events happened in the story.

Nina and Lee found the stranded whale.
↓
They told their grandfather about it.
↓
↓
The whale was helped and swam away.

Which of these belongs in the empty box?

A They went to Ocean World to get a veterinarian.

B Dr. Kaplow was a vet from the Wildlife Department.

C Grandpa called the Wildlife Department to report the whale.

D Lee thought it was a shark.

28 Which of these best describes how Nina felt when she watched the whale swim away?

   A Worried that the whale might be sick

   B Scared that the whale might wash back up on another beach

   C Sad that the whale was leaving

   D Happy that the whale was all right

29 Read the meanings below for the word <u>watch</u>.

> **watch** (woch)
>
> *verb* **1.** to look at someone or something attentively **2.** to guard or keep under surveillance
> *noun* **3.** a small timepiece **4.** an alert issued to the public by the National Weather Service

Which meaning best fits the way watch is used in paragraph 20?

   A Meaning 1

   B Meaning 2

   C Meaning 3

   D Meaning 4

30 Read the first sentence of the summary below.

> ### Summary of "Save the Whale!"
>
> **Nina and Lee see a beached whale on the shore.**

Which of the following completes the summary above?

   A Nina knows a lot about animals. She helps Lee identify the whale.

   B They tell their Grandpa, and he calls for help. The vet and the Wildlife Department officers help return the whale to the sea.

   C The sea is calm and beautiful. Nina and Lee decide that they are going to have a great beach day.

   D They return home, and their Grandpa makes them breakfast. They tell him all about the beached whale.

A Trip to Cahokia

1   Brian and his class were going on a field trip to see the Cahokia mounds. Brian was not convinced he would enjoy the trip because he did not know anything about early Native Americans. "Mounds of dirt can't be that interesting," he said to his friend Miko.

2   The bus pulled up in front of the school. Twenty students and three teachers piled on.

3   Brian and Miko found their seats. "We're on our way," Miko said. "We're going to see the oldest city in the United States. I can hardly wait."

4   "I don't know what to expect," said Brian. "I've never seen a mound built by Native Americans. Have you?"

5   "No," said Miko, "but I've read a little about them. I've seen some pictures, too. Still, that's nothing like seeing them up close."

6   When the bus pulled up, Miko and Brian and the other students climbed off the bus. They could see huge dirt and stone mounds in the distance. Miko's eyes sparkled like jewels in the sunshine as she looked at the ancient mounds. Brian gazed out at the huge mounds, and he broke into a grin.

7   Just then, a guide greeted the students. "Welcome to Cahokia," she said. "Here's a pamphlet that gives you some background about the Cahokia mounds. Please take a moment to read it before we begin our tour. It will help you to understand better the sights you are about to see."

The Mound Builders

8   Indian mounds were built as early as 7000 years ago. They were built as burial grounds and also as platforms to hold temples and houses for important chiefs. Thousands of Indian mounds still stand in the United States and Canada.

9   Building these mounds was no easy task. The workers had to carry large loads of dirt on their backs because they didn't have horses or oxen or wheeled carts at that time. Many of the mounds were huge, containing as much as several hundred tons of dirt, stone, and other materials.

10   Many different groups of Native Americans built mounds. Several groups lived in the valleys of the Mississippi and Ohio Rivers and in the Great Lakes region. The three main groups that built mounds were the Hopewell, Adena, and Mississippian peoples.

Page 1

Cahokia—The Largest Mississippian City

11   The Mississippian culture lasted from about 700 A.D. until the 1700s. This group of people lived mainly in the Mississippi Valley area in what is now the midwestern United States. These people built some of the earliest cities in North America.

12   Cahokia, near present-day Collinsville, Illinois (just eight miles from downtown St. Louis, Misssouri), was the largest Mississippian city. It was also the largest city at that time in North America.

13   Most other Native American communities of that period had only a few thousand people, but Cahokia had a population of almost 40,000. No other city had more than 24 mounds, but Cahokia had more than 100 mounds. Some of these mounds were small, and others were very large. Evidence suggests that no other Native American community of the time had a mound as grand as Monks Mound, the largest mound in Cahokia. Monks Mound is bigger around at the base than the Great Pyramid of Egypt. It is about 100 feet tall, or about the same height as a ten-story building. Covering roughly 16 acres, it is the largest earth mound in the United States.

Page 2

31 Why are Miko's eyes compared to jewels?

   A   They are large and round. ✗ No *is not that*

   B   They are very valuable. ✗ No *they are not valuable*

   C   They are brown. ✗ No *it doesn't say*

   D   They sparkle in the sunlight. ? *Yes it could be*

32 Which of these best describes how Brian feels after he gets off the bus at Cahokia?

   A   Bored because he thinks the mounds look silly ? *It could be*

   B   Happy because he thinks the mounds might be interesting to learn about ✗ No *is not happy*

   C   Worried because he thinks his friends are leaving without him ✗ No *doesn't say*

   D   Angry because he didn't want to go on this field trip ✗ *No doesn't say*

33 According to the pamphlet, where is Cahokia located?

   A   In Illinois ✗ *Is not in Illinois*

   B   In Missouri ✗ *Is not in Missouri*

   C   In Mississippi ? *Yes it says in the map*

   D   On the Missouri River ✗ *No is not that*

34 Look at the chart comparing Cahokia with other Native American communities.

Cahokia	Other Native American Communities
• Over 100 mounds	• No more than 24 mounds
• Population of 40,000	• Population of a few thousand people
• _____	• Did not have a grand mound

Which detail best completes the chart?

   A   Several groups lived there at one time ✗ *No is not that*

   B   Other communities did not have as many mounds or as many people living there ✗ *No it didn't tell you*

   C   Had the largest prehistoric earth mound in the U.S. ✗ *No doesn't say*

   D   Other communities had more platforms for temples ? *It could be*

#8

35 Which of these best describes how Miko feels when she gets off the bus?

A Anxious because she thinks Brian is not having fun

B Annoyed because she thinks Brian should have a better attitude

C Excited that she is going to get to explore the mounds

D Worried that she might not have time to see all the mounds

36 Read the meanings below for the word mound.

> **mound** (mound) *noun* **1.** an artificial elevation or bank of earth or stones **2.** any heap or pile of objects **3.** a small, natural elevation; hillock **4.** the slightly raised area in the center of the baseball diamond from which the pitcher pitches

Which meaning best fits the way mound is used in paragraph 8?

A Meaning 1

B Meaning 2

C Meaning 3

D Meaning 4

37 What can the reader tell about Brian from reading this story?

A Brian changes his mind about learning about Native American mounds.

B Brian decides that Native American mounds are not as interesting as he expected.

C Brian's teacher is surprised that Brian is going on the field trip.

D Brian's favorite subject is Native American history.

38 Look at this web of information from the pamphlet.

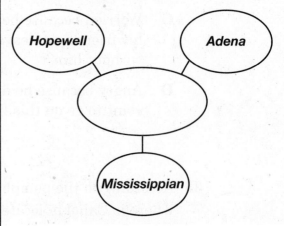

Which of these belongs in the empty circle?

A Native American mound builders

B Indian mounds in the United States

C Mound builders in the southern United States

D Earliest Native American cities

39 The pamphlet was written mainly to—

A inform readers about similarities between mounds in Illinois and Egypt

B entertain readers with a story about giant mounds

C persuade readers to build earth mounds

D inform readers about an important Native American historical site

40 In paragraph 13, one of the Cahokia mounds is compared to—

A European cities

B the Ohio River Valley

C the Great Lakes

D an Egyptian pyramid

P.13

Student Name _____

TAKS
Texas Assessment of Knowledge and Skills

Grade 4 Writing Practice Test
Revising and Editing

Val is a fourth grader at Bascomb Elementary School. She kept a journal during the summer. Here is one entry from her journal. Val is thinking about revising the journal entry for an assignment about one special day from her summer vacation. Read the journal entry and think about revisions Val might make if she uses it for her assignment. Then answer the questions that follow.

Monday, July 5

(1) Today is the third day of our island vacation, and I'm having the best time ever! (2) I slept so well last night. (3) And the sea breezes make me hungry! (4) I had a huge breakfast. (5) This whole morning I felt great. (6) I was full of energy.

(7) Early in the afternoon, I went swimming with my brother and sister. (8) Mom said we looked like three corks bobbing in the waves. (9) We played all afternoon in the surf. (10) Finally, my sister and me rode on our inflatable rafts.

(11) By 4 o'clock I very sleepy. (12) Mom suggested that I take a nap. (13) I was tired I could barely move. (14) Mom said I looked like a turtle leaving the beach. (15) When I got to the house, I went right to sleep!

(16) Tonight Dad showed us the pictures he took while scuba diving. (17) They showed all kinds of corals and seeweed. (18) Dad said the underwater plants were like a maze. (19) A diver who wasn't careful could easily get lost. (20) It must be even more amazing to go scuba diving in the Great Barrier Reef! (21) Dad's pictures also showed

beautiful fish. (22) There were red fish, green fish blue fish, and yellow fish. (23) Swimming together, they looked like a moving rainbow?

(24) I'm glad we came here for our vacation. (25) This is the greater vacation I've ever taken!

1 Which sentence could **BEST** be added after sentence 4?

  A Dad saw so many different kinds of fish when he went scuba diving!

  B Our family decided to go to Aruba for vacation.

  C I couldn't decide whether to have scrambled eggs or pancakes, so I had them both!

  D The sea breezes come in from the east.

2 Which sentence could **BEST** be added after sentence 9?

  A Then we built a sand castle together at the water's edge.

  B Portugal produces much of the world's cork.

  C We swim at my friend Jesse's pool sometimes.

  D Then we had fun in the ocean.

3 What change, if any, should be made in sentence 10?

  A Change *Finally* to **Finaly**

  B Change *me* to **I**

  C Change *rode* to **road**

  D Make no change

4 What is the **BEST** way to rewrite the ideas in sentence 13?

  A I was tired and could barely move me.

  B I was tired. I could not barely move.

  C I am tired that I can barely move.

  D I was so tired that I could barely move.

5 What change, if any, should be made in sentence 17?

  A Change *showed* to **shown**

  B Add a comma after **kinds**

  C Change *seeweed* to **seaweed**

  D Make no change

6 Which sentence does **NOT** belong in the journal entry?

  A Sentence 17

  B Sentence 18

  C Sentence 19

  D Sentence 20

7 What change, if any, should be made in sentence 22?

   A Change *There* to **Their**

   B Add a comma after *green fish*

   C Change *yellow fish* to **yellow fishes**

   D Make no change

8 What change, if any, should be made in sentence 23?

   A Change *looked* to **looks**

   B Change *rainbow* to **rainbough**

   C Change the question mark after *rainbow* to a period

   D Make no change

9 What change, if any, should be made in sentence 25?

   A Change *greater* to **greatest**

   B Change *I've* to **Iv'e**

   C Change *taken* to **took**

   D Make no change

10 Which of the following is **NOT** a complete sentence?

   A Sentence 2

   B Sentence 11

   C Sentence 17

   D Sentence 24

Bryce is a fourth grader at Taylor Elementary School. He is writing a story about a time that his friend found a lost dog. Read his story and think about corrections that are needed and improvements Bryce should make. Then answer the questions that follow.

Finding a home for Rusty

(1) "Rusty's a good name for you," said Angela, tossing a ball to the barking dog. (2) Rusty caught the ball. (3) He raced around the yard. (4) Finally he came back to Angela. (5) They went inside.

(6) "It's lucky Rusty gets along with bingo," said Angela's mom. (7) "But it's a week now since you found him. (8) I guess we're never going to locate his owner."

(9) Bingo, lying in the corner, raised his head from his paws.

(10) "Mom, I know we can't keep him," said Angela. (11) "We've got to find him a new home."

(12) "It can be your project," suggested Mom.

(13) Angela set out to find Rusty a new home. (14) First, she maked posters that said, "Great dog needs a new home." (15) Then she put up the posters in local store windows and on the bulletin boards at the supermarkets. (16) And on telephone poles around town. (17) Finally, she placed an ad in the pet section of the local newspaper. (18) Then the family waited.

(19) "I know some people would rather adopt puppys, but grown dogs make good pets, too," Angela said to her mom.

(20) Finally, a little girl from across town called. (21) "I saw your poster about that adorible dog," she said. (22) "My family would love to adopt Rusty."

(23) Angela smiled she knew she had found for Rusty a happy home.

1 What change, if any, should be made to the title of this story?

A Change *Finding* to **Findding** ✗

B Change *home* to **Home**

C Change *for* to **four** ✗

D Make no change ✗

2 What is the **BEST** way to combine sentences 2 and 3?

A Rusty caught the ball, he raced around the yard. ✗

B Rusty caught the ball and raced around the yard.

C Rusty caught the ball, and, raced around the yard. ✗

D Rusty caught the ball, raced, around the yard. ✗

5.2+3

3 What change, if any, should be made in sentence 6?

A Change *It's* to **Its** ✗

B Change *bingo* to **Bingo**

C Change *said* to **say** ✗

D Make no change ✗

5.6

4 The meaning of sentence 10 can be improved by changing *him* to—

A Rusty

B Bingo ✗

C both dogs ✗

D the ball ✗

5.10

5 What change, if any, should be made in sentence 11?

A Change *We've* to **Wev'e** ✗

B Change *new* to **knew** ✗

C Change the period after *home* to a question mark ✗

D Make no change

5.11

6 What change, if any, should be made in sentence 14?

A Change *maked* to **made**

B Change *said* to **says** ✗

C Change the period after *home* to a comma ✗

D Make no change ✗

5.14

7 What change, if any, should be made in sentence 19?

A Change *puppys* to **puppies**

B Change *grown* to **grone**

C Change *too* to **to**

D Make no change

8 What change, if any, should be made in sentence 21?

A Change *adorible* to **adorable**

B Change *adorible* to **most adorible**

C Add a comma after *poster*

D Make no change

9 What is the **BEST** way to rewrite the ideas in sentence 23?

A Angela smiled, she knew she had found for Rusty a happy home.

B Angela smiled, but she knew she had found Rusty a happy home.

C Angela smiled, she knew, she had found for Rusty a happy home.

D Angela smiled, She knew she had found a happy home for Rusty.

10 Which of the following is **NOT** a complete sentence?

A Sentence 12

B Sentence 16

C Sentence 18

D Sentence 22

Ravi is a fourth grader at Liberty Elementary School. Read his report about the invention of the bicycle and think about improvements he might make. Also watch out for spelling and grammar mistakes. Then answer the multiple-choice questions that follow.

Emilio Cáceres
Writing

3-2-10
calvert

The Bicycle

(1) Do you enjoy bicycle riding? (2) Then you should thank Baron Karl von Drais. (3) You probably don't know his name, but you know his invention. (4) Baron von Drais helped to create the bicycle. (5) In 1817, he invented a "walking machine" to help him get around. (6) This machine looked like the modern bicycle, except it didn't have pedals. (7) The person using it would push his or her feet. (8) This machine was hard to use and not very popular.

(9) In the 1860s, a better two-wheeled riding machine was invented. (10) This machine was known as the velocipede, it was also known as the "fast foot." (11) The rider sat on a seat close the large front wheel. (12) This machine was more poplar but not very comfortable. (13) In fact, people called it the "bone shaker."

(14) The bicycle as we know it was invented in 1898. (15) This type of bike was comfortable. (16) It was easy to use. (17) It was even comfortable for women who wore the long, heavy skirts that were fashionable then. (18) Some people like to wear bike shorts.

© Macmillan/McGraw-Hill

(19) However, some people say that bicycling helped change women's fashion. (20) Riding bicycles became so popular that women stopped wearing tight, uncomfortable clothing so that they could ride bicycles. (21) Riders today wear many different types of clothes, and the bicycles they ride come in many shapes and sizes.

1. The meaning of sentence 7 can be improved by changing *his or her feet* to

   A   the feet

   B   the rider's feet

   C   his and her feet

   D   his or her feet against the ground

   5.7

2. Which sentence does **NOT** belong in this paper?

   A   Sentence 2

   B   Sentence 8

   C   Sentence 12

   D   Sentence 18

3. What change, if any, should be made in sentence 8?

   A   Add commas before and after *and*

   B   Change *This* to *that*

   C   Change *was* to *were*

   D   Make no change

   5.8

4. What is the **BEST** way to rewrite the ideas in sentence 10?

   A   This machine was known as the "fast foot velocipede."

   B   This machine was known as the velocipede. This machine was also known as the "fast foot."

   C   This machine was known as the velocipede, or the "fast foot."

   D   This machine was also known as the "velocipede, fast foot."

   5.10

5. Which sentence could **BEST** be added after sentence 10?

   A   Do you have fast feet?

   B   Some people had trouble saying the name

   C   Bicycles are very popular in China.

   D   The front wheel of the velocipede was much bigger than the back wheel.

   5.10

6 What change, if any, should be made in sentence 11?

   A Change *close* to **close to**

   B Change *sat* to **seated**

   C Change *wheel* to **weel**

   D Make no change

S.11

7 What change, if any, should be made in sentence 12?

   A Add a comma before *not*

   B Change *very* to **vary**

   C Change *poplar* to **popular**

   D Make no change

S.12

8 What change, if any, should be made in sentence 13?

   A Remove the comma before *people*

   B Change *people* to **peeple**

   C Change *called* to **calling**

   D Make no change

S.13

9 Which sentence could **BEST** be added after sentence 13?

   A Because the "bone shaker" was so uncomfortable to ride, not many were produced or sold.

   B The velocipede was quite different from the scooterlike invention of Baron von Drais.

   C Many people rode in horse-drawn buggies in those days.

   D Sometimes people took trains to get from one place to another.

S.13

10 What is the **BEST** way to combine sentences 15 and 16?

   A This type of bike was comfortable, it was easy to use.

   B This type of bike was comfortable, but it was easy to use.

   C This type of bike was comfortable and it was, easy to use.

   D This type of bike was comfortable and easy to use.

S.15 & 16

Sasha is writing about a time when she was surprised. As you read her paper, think about changes she should make. Then answer the questions that follow.

A Stinging Adventure

(1) Last summer, our family went to see Aunt Bess and Uncle J. B. (2) They live on a beautiful, ten-acre farm near the appalachian Mountains.

(3) One day, Aunt Bess had a special chore for Becky and I. (4) She was getting ready to make jelly. (5) "Will you two pick grapes for me?" she asked.

(6) Aunt Bess gave Becky and me each a bucket. (7) The buckets were for the grapes. (8) Then she showed us where the grapevines were. (9) We headed off for our adventure.

(10) Right away, I saw a big bunch of purple grapes. (11) Becky was finding grapes, too. (12) I started hurrying to fill my bucket before Becky filled hers.

(13) I guess I not paying attention. (14) I was watching Becky's bucket, reaching into a bush, I felt a sharp pain. (15) I pulled my hand out of the bush. (16) Bees came flying out of their, too! (17) I must have disturbed a nest. (18) I ran to the house, crying, "Help! Bees!"

(19) Dad and Uncle J. B. came running from the barn. (20) Aunt Bess put some medicine on the sting. (21) After about an hour, I was feeling better. (22) Despite the fact that there be no grape jelly.

(23) The next time I picks grapes, I won't stick my hands into a bush!

What change, if any, should be made in sentence 2?

- **A** Add a comma after *live*
- **(B)** Change *appalachian* to *Appalachian*
- **C** Change *Mountains* to *mountains'*
- **D** Make no change

What change, if any, should be made in sentence 3?

- **A** Change *Aunt* to *aunt*
- **B** Change *had* to *has*
- **(C)** Change *I* to *me*
- **D** Make no change

What change, if any, should be made in sentence 5?

- **A** Add a comma before *for me*
- **B** Change *two* to *too*
- **C** Change *me* to *I*
- **(D)** Make no change

Which is the **BEST** way to combine sentences 6 and 7?

- **(A)** Aunt Bess gave Becky and me each a bucket for the grapes.
- **B** Aunt Bess gave Becky and me each a bucket for the grapes.
- **C** Aunt Bess gave Becky and me each a bucket, they were for the grapes.
- **D** Aunt Bess gave Becky and me each a bucket, but the buckets were for the grapes.

What change, if any, should be made in sentence 13?

- **(A)** Change *not* to *wasn't*
- **B** Change the period after *attention* to a question mark
- **C** Change *attention* to *attenshun*
- **D** Make no change

6 What is the **BEST** way to rewrite the ideas in sentence 14?

   A I was watching Becky's bucket, reaching into a bush, and I felt a sharp pain.

   B I watched Becky's bucket, reached into a bush, and felt a sharp pain.

   C As I was watching Becky's bucket and reaching into a bush, I felt a sharp pain.

   D I was watching Becky's bucket, reaching into a bush, and feeling a sharp pain.

7 What change, if any, should be made in sentence 16?

   A Change *too* to **two**

   B Change *their* to **there**

   C Change the exclamation point after *too* to a question mark

   D Make no change

8 Which sentence could **BEST** be added after sentence 19?

   A I really hate bees!

   B The barn was old and in desperate need of a new coat of paint.

   C My favorite cow, Daisy Mae, was in that barn.

   D Uncle J. B. went off to take care of the nest, and Dad took me into the house to find my aunt.

9 Which of the following is **NOT** a complete sentence?

   A Sentence 12

   B Sentence 15

   C Sentence 18

   D Sentence 22

10 What change, if any, should be made in sentence 23?

   A Change *picks* to **pick**

   B Remove the comma after *grapes*

   C Change *won't* to **won't never**

   D Make no change

TAKS
Texas Assessment of Knowledge and Skills

Grade 4 Writing Practice Test

Composition

Write about a time when you surprised someone.

The box below will help you write your composition. Then write your composition on another piece of paper.

REMEMBER TO—

❑ write about a time when you surprised someone

❑ include details about what you did and how the other person reacted

❑ use descriptive language so your reader can imagine what you are writing about

❑ check your spelling, capitalization, punctuation, grammar, and sentences

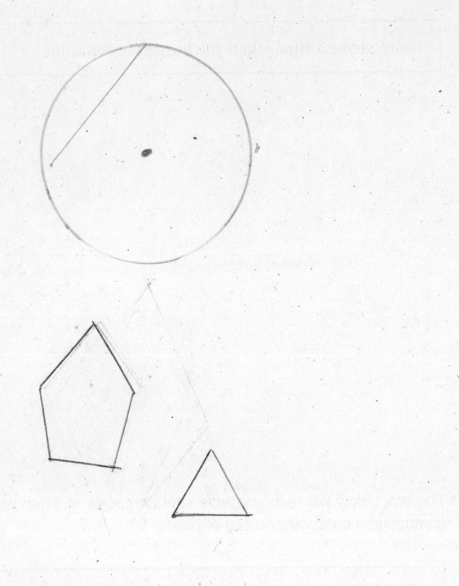